# Account Of An Expedition To The Interior Of New Holland

By

Lady Mary Fox

Double9 BOOKS

# Account Of An Expedition To The Interior Of New Holland

**by Lady Mary Fox**



ISBN: 978-93-59955-61-2

**Published by**

**DOUBLE 9 BOOKS**

2/13-B, Ansari Road
Daryaganj, New Delhi – 110002
info@double9books.com
www.double9books.com
Tel. 011-40042856

# ABOUT THE AUTHOR

Lady Mary Fox (19 December 1798 – 13 July 1864) was King William IV of the United Kingdom's illegitimate daughter by his mistress Dorothea Jordan. She went on to become a writer later in life. Mary FitzClarence was the fourth child and second daughter of Prince William, Duke of Clarence and St Andrews, and actress Dorothea Jordan, and was born in Bushy House. She has been described as "a fine looking, brown girl with a pleasant countenance and manners”. Charles Richard Fox, the eldest but illegitimate son of Lord Holland and Lady Webster, subsequently Lady Holland, courted her younger sister Elizabeth in 1820. His parents did not approve of the match, but they later approved of his relationship with Mary four years later. On June 19, 1824, the couple married in St George's, Hanover Square, London. Lady Holland was concerned that she may be "a sickly subject" and desired that her mother's "roturier blood might have mitigated the royal constitutions." On August 31, her mother-in-law wrote that her son, "though fond of her, he only considers her as an auxiliary to his medals and other possessions, not as a principal," but that "it will all do well; as she is very winning, and very firm, and sincerely fond of him." By 1827, the couple had made their home in Little Holland House.

# CONTENTS


CHAPTER I .......... 7

CHAPTER II .......... 16

CHAPTER III .......... 23

CHAPTER IV .......... 28

CHAPTER V .......... 35

CHAPTER VI .......... 40

CHAPTER VII .......... 45

CHAPTER VIII .......... 52

CHAPTER IX .......... 59

CHAPTER X .......... 63

CHAPTER XI .......... 73

CHAPTER XII .......... 78

CHAPTER XIII .......... 93

CHAPTER XIV .......... 100

# CHAPTER I

*Wonderful Discovery.—The Adventurers.—Marshy Lake.—The Canoe.—Troublesome Navigation.—Chain of Lakes.—Party of Natives.—Reception of the Travellers.—Singular People.—Early Emigrants.—The Settlement.—Exploring Party.—Encounter with Natives.—Native Allies.—Attack of Savages.—Defeat of the Assailants.—Savage Life.—Treaty of Peace.—Education of Savages.—Election of Senators.*

Our readers will, no doubt, be interested by the few particulars we have been able to collect of the late wonderful discovery, in the interior of New Holland, of a civilized nation of European origin, which had, in so remarkable a manner, been kept separate hitherto from the rest of the civilized world.

Mr. Hopkins Sibthorpe, who planned and conducted this singularly fortunate enterprise, was accompanied, it appears, in the expedition by another settler, Mr. William Jones, and Messrs. Thomas and Robert Smith (brothers), of the navy; who, together with Wilkins, a sailor, hired as their servant, constituted the whole party.

It was in the early part of August 1835 that these adventurous explorers took their departure from the settlement at Bathurst: this, as our readers are aware, is the last month of the winter of that hemisphere; though, from the greater mildness of the climate, it may be considered as spring. This season was chosen as the most suitable for an expedition in such a country as New Holland; in which, not only the heat of summer and autumn is often very oppressive, but also the scarcity of water is one of the most formidable impediments: and, on this occasion, a plentiful supply of water being essential, not only with a view to their personal wants, but also to the accomplishment of the peculiar plan they had resolved on trying, it was thought best to take an early advantage of the effects of the winter's rains.

Their plan was no other than to construct a canoe, to enable them to proceed in a direction in which farther progress had hitherto been precluded by a vast expanse of marshy lake. This, as our readers are probably aware, from the published narratives of former expeditions, is, in moist seasons, a sort of Mere, or shallow water, encumbered with aquatic plants; but in times of great drought is, for a considerable extent, dry, or consisting of mud rather than water; constituting a sort of swampy plain, so choked up with a rank vegetation of reeds and flags as to present an almost insuperable obstacle to the traveller.

In the present expedition, accordingly, it was determined to choose a time when there might be a sufficiency of water to enable the adventurous explorers to proceed in a canoe; and they accordingly carried with them one or two horses (which they proposed afterwards to turn loose)—the iron-work, and as much as was thought necessary of the frame of a canoe, which they proposed to put together and complete on their arrival on the margin of the lake. And as it was impossible to carry with them a sufficient store of provisions for the whole of their contemplated voyage, they boldly resolved to trust in great measure to their guns and fishing tackle, providing only a sufficiency of salt to preserve such game and fish as they might procure in their way.

The details of the expedition, curious and highly interesting as they are in themselves, we are compelled to omit, lest they should occupy the space wanted for a far more valuable and important portion of the narrative. It will be sufficient, therefore, to say, omitting particulars, that they were enabled to put their design in execution; and having constructed a kind of light flat-bottomed boat, of poles covered with bark (of the kind the natives use for their canoes), and fitted up with a slight awning, to afford shelter from the sun and the dews, they embarked on the above-mentioned shallow lake, and proceeded in a north-west direction; sometimes rowing, assisted occasionally by a sail, and oftener pushing themselves on with poles through the tangled aquatic plants which grew on the muddy bottom.

Their progress was at first tediously slow; but they were at no loss for provision, as the waters abounded with fish and wildfowl, of which they continued to obtain a sufficient supply throughout the voyage. After two days of troublesome navigation they found the water become deeper, and gained a sight of some elevated land towards the west, which they reached on the evening of the third day: they here found the lake not terminated, but confined within narrow limits by hills, for the most part of a rocky, sterile, and uninviting character: at length it became a broad river, flowing in a northerly direction, and serving evidently as a drain to the great expanse of lake they had passed. This gave them hopes of reaching (which was their great object) some large navigable river, which they might follow to the sea: they proceeded, therefore, though with considerable delay and difficulty from shoals and rapids, till, after more than two days' navigation, the high ground receded, and they found themselves entering on another great expanse of water, so extensive that, in pursuing their adventurous course nearly in the same direction, they were, for the greater part of one day, out of sight of land.

They now arrived at another course of rocky hills, of considerable elevation, through which the waters found an exit by a narrow gorge: through this they proceeded in a direction northwards for a considerable distance, when they found the river again expanding itself at intervals into a chain of lakes, smaller but deeper than those they had passed, and surrounded by a much more agreeable country, which continued to improve as they advanced. They landed in several places, and in one instance came in contact with a party of natives, who were of a less savage aspect than those in the vicinity of our settlements, and showed no signs of hostility, and much less of alarm and astonishment than had been expected. From this circumstance, and also from steel knives being in the possession of two or three of them, on which they appeared to set great value, it was conjectured that they must, in their wanderings, have, at some time or other, approached our settlements: their language, however, was perfectly unintelligible to Mr. Jones, though he had a considerable acquaintance with that of the natives near Sydney.

Some days after, as they continued their progress, they fell in with another party of natives, who excited still more wonder and speculation in our travellers, from their having among them ornaments evidently fashioned from the tusks of boars; these (as it was understood from the signs they made, in answer to the questions put to them by the same means) they described themselves as having hunted with their dogs, and speared. But all doubt was removed the next day, by the travellers actually obtaining a sight of a wild hog in the woods, and afterwards of a herd of wild cattle, which they distinctly saw with their glasses: these animals being well known not to be indigenous in New Holland, afforded strong indications of the vicinity of some European settlement; though, as they felt certain of being far distant from the coast, they were utterly lost in conjecture.

After proceeding in the manner above described, through a long chain of lakes connected by the river which they were continuing to navigate, through a country continually improving in beauty and fertility, and presenting a strong contrast to the dreary rocks and marshes they had left behind, they were at length surprised and gratified, on entering a lake somewhat more extensive than the last, to see several fishing-boats, the men in which they ascertained by their glasses to be decently clothed, and white men. They ventured to approach and to hail them; and, to their unspeakable surprise and delight, they received an answer in English: the English was, indeed, not precisely similar to their own, but not differing so much from it as many of our provincial dialects; and in a short time the two parties were tolerably intelligible to each other.

We are compelled to pass over the interesting detail of the meeting, which was equally gratifying and surprising to both the parties; of the eager curiosity of their mutual inquiries; and of the hospitable invitation given, and, as may be supposed, joyfully accepted by the travellers. Accompanying their hosts in one of the fishing-boats, they found before them, on turning the point of a wooded promontory which had intercepted their view, a rich and partially cultivated country, interspersed with cheerful-looking villages, having much of an English air of comfort; though the whole was in a far ruder condition than much of what they saw afterwards, as the point they had reached was the extreme skirt of a comparatively recent settlement.

The reception they met with was most friendly and every way refreshing, after an anxious and toilsome journey of above a month. They found themselves, on the second day after their arrival in the colony, the guests of the chief magistrate of a neat town of considerable size, where they were surrounded by visitors from all parts, eager to obtain and to afford information, and overwhelming them with pressing invitations.

We are compelled to pass over the particulars of the several steps by which the travellers arrived at the knowledge of the singular country and people in the midst of which they found themselves. We have only space for a brief summary of the results.

They found themselves, then, in a nation of European, and chiefly, though not entirely, of English extraction, which had had no intercourse with Europe, or with any other portion of the civilized world, for nearly three centuries. Their numbers were estimated at between three and four millions; and they were divided into eleven distinct communities, existing in a sort of loosely federal union, or rather in a friendly relation, sanctioned and maintained by custom more than by any formal compact. And they found these several states, though in some respects differing in their governments and other institutions, agreeing in the manifestation of a high degree of civilization, considering the disadvantage they laboured under in their seclusion from the rest of the world. "Many points too," says Mr. Sibthorpe, in his journal, "in which they differ the most widely from the customs and institutions of the people from which they sprang, are such as can hardly be reckoned marks of barbarism, even by those who regard them with surprise, and even with disapprobation; but are rather the result of the singular and, as some would consider them, whimsical notions of the extraordinary persons who took the lead among the first settlers."

These were two men of the name of Müller; one a German, settled in England, and the other his nephew, the son of an Englishwoman. The former appears to have been one of those unions of enthusiastic wildness, brilliant genius, and sanguine credulity which periods of great excitement—such as the commencement of the Reformation—are often found to call forth. He possessed great eloquence, and a power of exercising an unbounded influence over minds of a certain description. His nephew, with much of the uncle's eccentricity, united a much clearer judgment, and seems gradually to have established a complete ascendancy over the mind, first of his uncle, and ultimately of all his followers; and to have used his influence in a manner which indicates most enlarged public spirit, and a great mixture, at least, of political wisdom.

It appears, that during the various tumults which took place during the early periods of the Reformation, several persons in England, and some in Germany, (the parties holding communication through the means of Müller and his connexions in both countries,) meditated a removal to some distant region, in which they should escape finally from strife and oppression, and establish a civil and religious community on such principles as they were fondly cherishing. After the proposal and rejection of various schemes, and after many delays and disappointments, the projected departure in search of a new settlement took place, under the guidance of their enthusiastic and adventurous leader. Instead of proceeding to America, as had been originally proposed, they were induced by some glowing descriptions they had heard, but which proved to consist chiefly of fable or exaggeration, to seek for the long-famed southern continent, the "Terra Australis Incognita."

The curious and interesting particulars of their voyage, their various adventures, disappointments, and reiterated attempts, we are compelled to pass over. The result was their being ultimately driven by a storm on the coast of New Holland, somewhere, it is supposed, between lat. 10 and 20 south, and lon. 130 and 140 east, where one out of the four ships was wrecked on a coral reef, and two of the others driven ashore with considerable damage. They saved, however, not only their lives, but nearly all their property, including the live stock with which they had provided themselves; and it appears that their first idea was to repair their vessels, and proceed along the coast, in an endeavour to find a suitable spot for a settlement; the part on which they were cast being not only barren and uninviting but excessively marshy. This last circumstance compelled them to forego their design; for a fever broke out, and affected so many of them that they lost no time in removing to a healthier situation, eight or nine miles from the coast. Here the sick speedily recovered; and, as the spot seemed highly salubrious, though for the most part barren, with only a small proportion of land fit for cultivation near the banks of small rivers, they proceeded to build log-houses and cultivate the land; designing to make their settlement either temporary or permanent, as circumstances might determine.

Their decision was ultimately fixed by means of the intercourse they succeeded in establishing with a native tribe. Mutual good-will and confidence having been completely established between the settlers and the natives (chiefly, as it should seem, through the judicious exertions of the younger Müller),—and an increasing knowledge of each other's language having established a free communication between the parties,—the settlers were interested by the glowing colours in which their new friends described a region in the interior, which they—that is, some of the very individuals who spoke of it, and the ancestors of the rest,—had formerly inhabited, and from which successive portions of their tribe had been from time to time expelled by more powerful hostile tribes. They were anxious to induce their European neighbours to settle there themselves, and enable them to reinstate themselves in their ancient abode. They easily perceived the vast superiority which European arts and arms would give to their new allies over enemies who had proved too powerful for themselves, and they hoped through their aid to re-establish themselves in a country which they had quitted with regret.

Moved by their representations, the settlers despatched two active young men, in company with some native guides, to explore this highly-vaunted region; they proceeded accordingly, nearly in a direct line from the coast, to a range of mountains, about ninety or a hundred miles in the interior, which they surmounted, not without difficulty, and then found themselves in an elevated plain of a most sterile character, extending for more than a hundred miles in the same direction: this they traversed with some difficulty, and arrived at another chain of rocky mountains, forming a still more formidable barrier, which they would have had great difficulty in surmounting but for the local knowledge of their guides.

On passing this, however, they were rewarded by the view of a most extensive and delightfully fertile region, watered with numerous streams from these mountains, and interspersed with beautiful lakes. The whole appearance of the country fully justified the descriptions given; and the accounts of these first explorers were so favourable that a second expedition was undertaken, with a view to a more complete examination of the country, by young Müller himself and four others, who passed a considerable time in exploring the district, not without some narrow escapes from the hostility of some of the wandering native tribes; and the result of their examination was so favourable, that the settlers were induced to come to the resolution of finally removing the colony to the interior.

This, after due preparation, they accomplished, moving in two separate divisions; the first consisting of the greater part of the most active of the adult males, both of the Europeans and their native allies, who were to prepare habitations, and break up land for tillage, &c. ready to receive the rest after an interval of some months. The entire removal was completed in the course of the third year from their first arrival on the coast. Their numbers appear to have been between three and four hundred, in all, of white people, besides a somewhat smaller number of natives; the country in which they had first settled admitting of only a small and scattered population, of tribes subsisting by the chase.

Very soon after taking possession of their new abode they were attacked, in spite of all their endeavours to preserve peace, by the native tribes of the interior, moved by their inveterate animosity against their ancient enemies: the settlers, however, gained an easy and complete victory in every encounter; their fire-arms, though only the old-fashioned, clumsy matchlocks of those days, being sufficient to strike terror into savages unacquainted with gunpowder; though, independent of their guns, their bows would have given them a decided superiority. It is well known how skilful and how formidable were the English archers of those days; and they could annoy the natives, among whom the bow is unknown, at three times the distance to which these could throw their spears. The native allies also, having been taught by the Europeans to use the bow, which, even in their less skilful hands, had an advantage over the spear,—and being also furnished with cutlasses, hatchets, and steel heads to their pikes,—now proved greatly an overmatch for their former conquerors, who had only wooden swords and bone-headed spears.

A peace ensued, which, however, was for several years interrupted from time to time by predatory incursions and irregular renewals of hostilities. This state of things, with all its inconveniences, appears to have had the advantage of cementing the friendship between the settlers and their native allies; each party feeling the other's importance for security against a common enemy. The whites, accordingly, seem to have been assiduous and successful in civilizing these natives, with whom they were thus thrown into close contact.

Ultimately, the colony was delivered from all danger from the hostile tribes by an event which threatened disaster. A formidable combination was secretly formed among all the tribes for a considerable distance round, for the purpose of making a united attack, by surprise, with all their forces. It was so far successful that a band, far outnumbering all that the settlers could muster, unexpectedly attacking one of their villages, obliged the inhabitants to fly in the utmost haste, and spread the alarm through the whole colony. This success, however, proved their ruin; for, with the genuine improvidence of savages, instead of rapidly pushing forward their forces, they eagerly fell to plundering the various stores, especially of provisions, which had been abandoned; and, as an army of savages is never well provided with a commissariat, gladly betook themselves to feasting on what they found.

Among other things, was a large supply of beer; for the settlers had brought with them, and successfully practised, the art of brewing, with which they had been familiar at home. Wine they had not as yet attained to, though they had begun the cultivation of the vine, as well as of several other European fruit-trees. The savages indulged in the liquor with characteristic excess; and, while they were lost in intoxication, set fire, either accidentally or intentionally, to the wooden houses and stacks with which they were surrounded. The fire raged fiercely in all directions; and most of the men were too much stupified with liquor to escape the flames, and were either stifled or burnt; a considerable number, however, were rescued by the settlers, who had by this time come together, and who at once saved and took prisoners most of the survivors, who were too helplessly drunk for either resistance or flight.

This event, which at once and for ever broke the power of their enemies, has been ever since annually commemorated in the colony; a day of solemn thanksgiving being concluded by the lighting of large bonfires in the evening, by parties who pass round among themselves a spear, such as the natives use, and a cup of beer, of which each tastes, in memory of their deliverance. This festival which the Müllers instituted, accompanying the celebration with apposite reflections on drunkenness and its effects, has probably tended, along with other circumstances, to keep up an almost universal habit of sobriety throughout the colony.

This interesting portion of their early history, thus impressed on their minds and familiarized to their thoughts from childhood, creates an indelible association of the idea of drunkenness, not only with those of helplessness and disaster, but also with that of the character of brutish and stupid *savages*. Indeed, in several other points also, our travellers found the idea of *savage* life so associated with some others in the minds of these people, as to influence considerably their conduct and habits of thought. They have a deep-seated and habitual contempt for every thing which, according to their notions, savours of barbarism; and this shows itself in many points, which to a modern European would be likely to appear whimsical. The younger Müller, though indefatigable in his kindness towards the native tribes, appears to have cherished this feeling in his own people. He laboured strenuously to reclaim and civilize the savages, and was equally anxious to guard against the reverse process—the approximation of the white men towards the habits of the savages: and, as he seems to have been a very able though eccentric man, and possessed boundless influence over the colonists, who were under his government for above half a century, he succeeded in effectually stamping his own character on the nation, and perpetuating his institutions.

The hostile tribes, after the above event, surrendered at discretion; and they consented (those of them who had a considerable proportion of able-bodied men remaining alive) to remove beyond a certain specified boundary, far beyond the then limits of the colony; but several tribes, which now consisted almost entirely of women and children, and were consequently hardly capable of providing for themselves, were, at their own entreaty, received as subjects, and incorporated, along with the previously-allied natives, into the body of the settlers.

The European and aboriginal races became in time completely blended together; for it appears to have been one of the principles most earnestly maintained and inculcated by their extraordinary leader, to allow of no hereditary degradation; no subjection of one race of men to another on the ground of colour or caste, but to make all subjects of the state necessarily admissible to the rights of citizenship. Yet, on the other hand, he was well aware of the actual inferiority of the aborigines as individuals and as a race, and was fully alive to the evil of placing inferior men on a level with those morally and intellectually superior. The maxim, accordingly, which he continually dwelt on, and laboured to embody in practice, was, that it is not the colour of the skin, but the heart and head, that makes a man savage or civilized. Education, accordingly, was the means adopted for reclaiming and for preserving men from barbarism: and examinations, to ascertain how far each had profited by the education bestowed, were made the test for admissibility into the highest public stations.

This principle has been in great measure adhered to in the several states into which the settlement was afterwards divided, though differing from each other in many respects in their forms of government. And yet, as Müller used himself to observe, one man may be much superior in fitness for certain public offices to another, who may be far beyond him in proficiency in a prescribed course of studies, and in everything that can be ascertained in any regular examination; but then, he used to add, when you come to a greater number, one hundred men well taught will always be superior to a hundred untaught, and fitter to govern the community. In all the states, accordingly, their senates are always required to consist of men who have given proof of their proficiency in a prescribed course of study; but these are left free to choose, and sometimes do choose, for the discharge of important offices, men who are inferior in this respect, but qualified by natural sagacity and practical habits of business.

# CHAPTER II

*Increase of the Settlement.—Separation of the States.—Ecclesiastical Communities.—Concord among Sects.—Houses and Towns.—Penal Colonies.—Southlanders' Hospitality.—Mode of receiving Company.—Feasts.—Animal Food.—Tame Animals.—Surprise at English Customs.—Carnivorous Propensity.—Lighting the Streets.—City of Bath.*

The settlement, on being thus (about five or six years from its commencement) freed from all external molestation, increased in prosperity, and extended itself rapidly in several directions inland. Towards the sea they had no temptation to advance; being separated from it by an extensive district of great sterility, and of difficult passage. Inward, the abundance of fertile land, and the numerous lakes with which our travellers had been struck, and which afforded easy intercourse even between settlements at a considerable distance, invited them to overspread the country as fast as their rapidly-increasing population required. Their numbers seem to have advanced at about the same rate as those of some of the North-American settlements.

The division into separate states was not, as the travellers found to their surprise, the result of discord, but had been planned and commenced by their founder himself. He had, it seems, foreseen, or fancied that he foresaw, an ultimate necessity for such a separation; and he judged it best that it should begin even in his own lifetime, before there was any advantage in it, except that of setting an example and establishing a precedent for amicable separation. He founded, accordingly, within forty years from their first settling, a second perfectly independent community, on the opposite side of the lake, near which the first had been located. The original settlement still forms one of the states, and retains the name of Müllersfield, which it received from the founders: the new one, from its singular beauty of situation, he called Eutopia (fine place), probably with something of a covert allusion also to the well-known fabulous Utopia (no place). The most perfect friendliness and freedom of intercourse continued between the two states; and, without owning any common authority, they consulted together, like any two individual neighbours who are on friendly terms, respecting any matters in which they had a common concern: and the principles of the procedure having been clearly laid down, and practically established, the example was afterwards repeatedly followed as the colonization extended itself; and fresh swarms, as it were, issued forth, till the number of the separate states amounted to eleven.

A similar principle has been acted on with respect to ecclesiastical communities. The number of separate churches amounts to no less than seventeen; though some of these consist chiefly of converted native tribes, together with the missionaries residing among them. These churches are, of course, not coextensive with the several states, but on the footing of the early churches founded by the apostles, who instituted several distinct ones,—for instance, in the single province of Macedonia; viz. those of Philippi, Thessalonica, Berœa, &c. They are all, and have ever been, with a few temporary exceptions, in concord and communion with each other, but under distinct governments, and differing in some non-essential customs and institutions. They seem to have made good a favourite maxim of Müller's on that subject;—that men are always most likely to live in friendly agreement in essentials, when they are not so closely connected as to be obliged to agree in matters intrinsically indifferent. "Two men," he used to observe, "who may be very friendly as neighbours, might quarrel, if they were obliged to live together, as to the hour at which they should dine,—the keeping of the windows open or shut, &c.;—in which one party would necessarily be compelled to give way to the other: whereas they may be very good friends while each follows his own taste in such matters."

We shall subjoin such scattered extracts as our space will admit, of those portions of our travellers' Journal which illustrate the more strange and singular particulars of the habits of this interesting people.

Nearly all their houses—in the towns, all, without exception—are flat-roofed, like those in the East; whether from a fancy of imitating the custom they read of in Scripture, or for the convenience of having an airy unconfined place to walk or sit on. In the towns, there is, as in those of the East, a thoroughfare for foot-passengers along the tops of the houses; and, in the larger towns, the streets are crossed occasionally by light bridges.

The houses in the towns, and all but the meaner sort of cottages in the newly-settled part of the country, are without any chimneys opening to the air: the smoke from the fireplaces of one or two, or more, adjoining houses, passes into a sort of chamber (swept from time to time), from which it is forced out by machinery into a flue branching off into pipes, which carry it back to the bottom of each fire; so that it burns its own smoke. When the visitors were describing to some Eutopians the European towns, these people remarked that London, for instance, though so much improved since the times of which they had historical records from their ancestors, must still have a very smoky atmosphere; and that, to walk along the streets, shut in by houses on both sides, must be very unpleasant, for want of open prospect and free circulation of air.

It was with much difficulty that these people were brought to understand the nature of the colony from which their visitors came; not that they were in general dull of apprehension, but they could scarcely satisfy themselves that they had rightly understood the accounts given them. To people a new settlement with convicted criminals,—to form a new nation of the scum and refuse of mankind,—appeared to them so preposterous, that for some time they could not help supposing they must have misunderstood their informants. "To bring together a number of villains," they said, "to a country where good character is not the rule, but the exception, allowing them free intercourse with each other must be the most effectual mode of hardening and confirming them in wickedness, and entailing the same character on successive generations:" and though it was explained to them that one great object of the plan was to reform the criminals, the accounts which truth constrained their visitors to give of the actual state of morals in the colony did not seem to satisfy them. They had wondered at first, they said, that such a scheme should have been originally thought of, and now they wondered still more that it should be persevered in.

The travellers were entertained with the kindest and most liberal hospitality, according to the notions of the Southlanders (such is the general name by which the inhabitants of all the states distinguish themselves from their European ancestors and other Europeans); but their hospitality differs considerably from ours. When residing as guests with any family, they partook of the family meals; but when invited to a party, as they frequently were, to meet the principal gentry of the neighbourhood,—who were anxious both to show attention to the strangers and to gratify their own curiosity,—it was found that there is no such thing in this country as what we call a dinner-party; that is, the company did not sit down together to a regular meal, but partook of refreshments something more of the character of an English luncheon, which was provided in all the superior houses in a separate room. The guests dropped into this eating-room irregularly, and seating themselves in small promiscuous parties at small tables set out there, were served by the attendants with the various dishes provided. They stayed as long as they pleased; conversed occasionally with their neighbours, as we do at an irregular luncheon, and returned to the "company-room" (as it is called), without ceremony, whenever they chose. No refreshments were brought into this last, except such as correspond to what we have at evening parties,—such as cakes, lemonade, wine and water, ices (in those districts which are near the mountains), dried or fresh fruits, &c.: this they consider as what they call the most "honourable"—what we should call "stylish"—mode of receiving company.

When our habits were described to them, they expressed their wonder that a civilized people should *make feasts as the savages do.* "The half-reclaimed native tribes," they said, "invite their friends whom they wish to honour to a solemn feast, at which, having provided a large quantity of their best provisions and liquor, and exerted what skill they have in cookery, the guests all seat themselves, with sundry formalities, round the food that is dressed, and regale themselves altogether; but with the Southlanders such an arrangement as this is only adopted as a convenience, when there is a large number of persons to be fed in the least troublesome way." They accordingly promised, laughingly, to take their visitors to something like an English dinner-party; and the party to which they invited them (it was during the season of hay harvest) consisted of about two dozen mowers, with several of their wives and children, seated round a long table, with the master at the head of it, and supping on an ample supply of substantial food, served up in five or six huge dishes.

The cookery among the higher classes is for the most part plain and simple, and the few who have refined much upon the luxuries of the table are exposed to something of the same sort of contemptuous ridicule that the being called a dandy incurs among us. But a circumstance which early attracted the attention of the visitors was, that they found the animal food to consist (besides eggs, cheese, and various preparations of milk) entirely of fish and game. The pork, which they often met with, they found to be always the flesh of the wild swine: these were derived from those brought over by the first settlers, who turned them all loose into the woods; and the chase of the wild-boar is eagerly pursued by many of the gentry. Wild cattle are also met with in some parts, descended from such as had accidentally strayed; and the flesh of these is eaten, as well as that of the kangaroo, emu, and other indigenous animals: but the visitors one day, in the course of conversation in the eating-room, expressed their surprise at having never seen any mutton served up, though sheep were not uncommon. The Southlanders had never heard the word mutton; but, when it was explained to them that it meant the flesh of the sheep, they replied, "That they kept their sheep very carefully for their wool, and that there were no wild sheep in the country: but when it was explained to them that we kept both sheep and oxen chiefly for the purpose of feeding on their flesh, they were both astonished and disgusted that we should have retained such a *barbarian* custom (for they regard themselves as many degrees more civilized than their European ancestors) as that of killing and eating domestic animals."

It was urged (and they freely admitted it) that the loss of life is no greater to a tame than to a wild animal: "That is true," they said, "as far as the *animal* is concerned; but it makes a great difference to *our* feelings. A tame animal is a sort of friend, a member of the family: it seems a sort of treacherous breach of hospitality to kill in cold blood a creature which you have reared and fed from its birth, and then devour its flesh." They expressed still more surprise (for they are keen sportsmen) at learning that some Europeans were vehement in their censures of hunting, fowling, and fishing, as cruel; and yet fed without scruple on beef and mutton. "We declare war," they said, laughing, "perhaps an unjust war, against wild animals, and kill them as enemies; but you assassinate your friends."—"We urged," says the journalist, "the necessity of keeping within bounds the numbers of our domestic animals; and expressed our apprehension that the Southlanders would in time find themselves quite overstocked with sheep, oxen, and fowls." They replied at the moment, merely, "that no such apprehension had ever occurred to them."

But, on returning to what we should call the drawing-room, we soon found that much interest was excited by the accounts of what appeared to this most singular people our strange custom. We were surrounded by ladies, who inquired, with an amusing mixture of good-humoured ridicule, wonder, and horror, into all the particulars respecting mutton; and one lady surprised us by asking, among other things, what kind of flesh was that of horses, dogs, and cats, and by what name we called it. When informed that, though we kept these animals, we never thought of eating them, she replied, "Why, I had understood that you ate the *flesh of domestic animals*, and that you found it *necessary* to do so, for fear of their *overstocking you with their numbers*! How comes it that you are not overrun with horses, dogs, and cats?" To say the truth, we were rather dumbfounded by this question; having, in fact, assigned as a reason what we had been accustomed to hear and repeat without any examination into its soundness. We could only allege that, in all these points, we conformed to what had always been the practice of our ancestors and theirs, and of almost all other nations: in this we were borne out by the testimony of those of the company who were well read in antiquities.

Several of these people, indeed, are good scholars, and well acquainted with the history (as far as was known three hundred years ago) of other nations, besides their own. They adverted to the descriptions of Homer's heroes: one of them would, when about to entertain his friends, have a sheep brought into his tent, cut its throat with his own royal hands, and then, with a skilful hand,—which the poet never fails to celebrate,—cut it up into slices and broil them on skewers over a charcoal fire. They remembered, also, the accounts given of some East-Indian tribes, who, when their relatives are grown old and infirm, kill them, to save them from lingering decay, and hold a pious and solemn feast on their flesh. But as these customs had worn away in the early progress of civilization, they wondered that a still further refinement had not, among us, confined the carnivorous propensity of man to wild animals exclusively, and led us, as it had them, to regard with disgust the eating of (as they expressed it) one of the family, whose eggs, milk, labour, or wool had long ministered to our comforts.

The description of our cities in their present condition, as contrasted with that of the sixteenth century, and of our whole mode of life, was exceedingly interesting to these people; but nothing did they admire more than our description of the gas-lights. In the midst, however, of their enquiries and admiration, one sly-looking old gentleman observed, "that if we would honour him with a visit in his city of Bath (capital of a state of the same name), he would excite even our admiration by the spectacle of an illumination still more splendid." In our visit there, where we were most kindly received, our host walked through the streets with us, showing us the principal buildings, and introduced us into the Senate-house, where the public business was going on.

On our return to his house, he asked us (this was about seven o'clock in the morning) what we thought of the lighting of the streets. We answered, that we observed neither any lighting of them, nor need of it, as it was a bright sunshine. "And is not this," said he, "as good a light as your gas? We have not," he added, "gone so far as you in arts; but we have the advantage of you in availing ourselves of the gifts of nature; for, as you must have observed, we are all alert and about our business at day-break; while you, by your own account, allow three or four hours of daylight in the spring and summer to be utterly wasted, while you are abed; and then go about your business at night, like owls and bats, but without their advantage of being able to see in the dark; so that you are forced to light yourselves with gas. It was," said he, "a very ingenious contrivance you were telling us of t'other day, by which you distil fresh water from the sea; but pray do you, when there are plenty of fresh springs, let all the water run to waste, that you may have the triumph of distilling from the brine?"

We endeavoured to explain to him the causes of our late hours; but we were astounded when he had made us compute the saving in oil, and gas, and tallow, which might be effected by a general resolution to *use daylight as far as it would go.*

The city at which this conversation took place is named from its celebrated warm baths, supplied by springs issuing from a mountain in the vicinity; one of the greatest curiosities in the country, both from the natural phenomena it exhibits (being evidently an extinct volcano), from which it received its name of Mount Peril, and from the extraordinary tradition of the superstitious ordeal formerly connected with it.

# CHAPTER III

*Duels.—Judicial Combats.—Existing Code of Honour.—Appeal to Arms.—Discussion on Duelling.—Mount Peril.—Noxious Vapours.—The Cavern.*

The visit of the travellers to Mount Peril, in the state of Bath, was preceded, and in some measure probably caused, by a conversation casually occurring on the subject of duels; and the notes taken of this, it may be as well first to lay before the reader.

Much inquiry and mutual communication appear to have taken place, as was to be expected, between the Southlanders and their guests respecting the institutions and manners of their respective countries; and among others the subject of duelling, as prevailing among the Europeans and Americans, happened one day to be introduced in a mixed company. A large proportion of the younger persons present expressed their astonishment that a people pretending to civilization should fight out their disputes "like the savages." This expression, as appears from several of the notices already recorded, was perpetually in their mouths; and some added, that the savages in their code of honour had the advantage of the Europeans. The New-Hollanders in these parts have, it seems, in respect of their duels, similar customs to those that have been observed by our settlers.

It has long been known that the aborigines of New South Wales leave all quarrels between individuals to be settled by a solemn judicial combat, the community interfering no farther than to see fair play. But their notions of fair play differ considerably from ours. If it, indeed, does not appear clearly which is the party aggrieved, they fight it out, man to man; the tribe being present as bystanders, while the combatants engage with spears or waddies (wooden swords) till the *satisfaction* is complete. But if one of the parties is adjudged to have the preponderance of justice on his side, he is allowed to bring a friend with him, as an auxiliary; and in very flagrant cases, even two or more, according to the character of the offence to be avenged.

In all cases, the offending party, however clear his guilt may be, is allowed to fight for his life; but in some cases, of course, against such odds as render it next to impossible he should escape. This, the Southlanders observed, was a degree better than the European duels, in which the regulations of our code of honour require the parties, however palpably one of them may be in the wrong, to meet on equal terms, or with an inequality only in favour of the one who may chance to be the better shot or swordsman.

Others of the company entered more fully into the discussion of the general grounds on which duelling is to be reprobated, being cordially joined in their censure by Mr. Jones, who urged the objections, with which every one is familiar, against the wickedness of taking away a fellow-creature's life, and exposing one's own, in revenge for a trifling affront—the absurdity of calling it a satisfaction to stand to be shot at, and other such topics, which it is unnecessary to enlarge on, as they may be read in numerous essays and tales, and heard at every tea-table.

The Messrs. Smith, on the other hand (naval men, as has been already mentioned) took the other side, and endeavoured to vindicate the existing code of honour. They urged that it is needless and nugatory to go about to prove that a duel is a bad thing, and that to censure the laws of honour on that ground is as unfair as to censure the law of the land on the ground that imprisonment and hanging are evils, these being the penalties denounced against a violation of the laws.

The requisition to expose one's life in a duel is, in like manner, the penalty denounced against a violation of the rules established in the society of gentlemen. The law of honour, they said, does not enjoin men to seek a duel as a desirable thing, but, on the contrary, to act in such a manner as to preclude all occasion for an appeal to arms; and that the penalty which any system of rules holds out against the violation of them should be regarded as something to be carefully avoided: this, so far from being an objection to the system, is essential to its maintenance. As for the unfairness of putting the injured and injuring party on a level, *that* they did not deny; but contended that it was an unavoidable evil, as in the case of war between two independent states. That every war is an evil,—that in every war one party must be in the wrong, and very often both: all this is universally admitted, but all this does not answer the practical question, whether, on the ground that war is an evil, a state should submit, and proclaim itself ready to submit, to any extent of encroachment and aggression from foreign nations without resistance. "If you go to war," it might be urged, "with those who have wronged you, you put yourself on equal terms with the wrong-doer, and are likely to suffer as much or more than the offending party." "Very true," it might be answered, "but we cannot help that; if we could, we would make all the evil of the war fall on the nation that has injured us; but as it is, we must do the best we can to deter our neighbours from injuring us: having no common superior to appeal to, we have no alternative but to fight for our rights, or to be insulted and oppressed with impunity."

When it was urged in reply, that, though nations have not, individuals have, a common authority to appeal to—that of the community to which they belong, this was roundly denied; and it was contended that the appeal to single combat does not take place in cases when the law of the land provides adequate redress, but in those only where it either cannot or will not afford any, or any but such as would be a mere mockery to the feelings of the sufferer. A man, they urge, does not challenge any one for robbing him of his purse, or for firing his barn, but for injuries of quite a different description, far more grievous to one moving in a certain circle of society, but which the law either refuses to take cognizance of at all, or for which it provides such redress as would aggravate the evil by rendering the sufferer ridiculous. Now a man resigns to the community his natural right of personal self-defence on the implied condition that the community shall protect him; and in cases, therefore, where it either cannot, or will not, fulfil this condition, his original natural right remains unimpaired. Thus, when a man is suddenly assaulted by a robber, he is free to defend his person and property as well as he can; and on the same principle, when the injury is of such a character as the law will not, or cannot, defend him from, he is left to guard his own honour with his own hand.

As to the evils resulting from duels, they observed that it is most unfair not to take into account—though to calculate would be impossible—the immense amount of evils prevented, and which there is reason to suppose would take place but for the apprehension of a duel. The insolence, the falsehood, the slander, the base and the overbearing conduct, which are daily kept in check in many thousands of persons by the recollection that there is such a thing as being "called out" for such behaviour, is what no one can compute with any approach to accuracy; these being preventive and negative effects, and therefore incapable of being calculated, and liable to be underrated.

Some idea, however, they added, may be formed of these effects of the laws of honour by looking to the conduct of those classes of persons who are exempted from them. The ancient Greeks and Romans, for instance, who are cried up as exempt from this Gothic barbarism, were accustomed, as we see from the specimens of their orators that have come down to us, publicly to revile each other in the grossest language. The Mahometans also, of all ranks, appear to be, with few exceptions, very much what Europeans would characterize by the term "blackguards;" and the same description seems very applicable to the people of the Celestial empire, from the haughty mandarin downwards.

In Europe, again, said these gentlemen, we see that those among the higher classes—viz. ladies and clergymen, (it is to be presumed the Messrs.

Smith had met with unfavourable specimens of these, and were rashly judging from such specimens,)—who are exempt from this law, are apt to avail themselves of that exemption by indulging themselves in the use of such language, and in such violation of truth and of decorum in their attacks on opponents as a layman would be deterred from by the apprehension of personal danger; so that, on the whole, it was contended that the evil of the lives lost in duels—an extremely small number—may be reckoned a cheap price paid by society for the advantages of civilized and well-regulated manners. And, after all, it was added, even that evil is not to be laid to the charge of the law of honour as a necessary accompaniment, since, if all persons adhered constantly to the rules of good society, there would never be occasion for a duel; in the same manner as there would never be occasion, if all men would comply with the law of the land, for any of the penalties of the law to be actually inflicted.

An old gentleman named Christopher Adamson, of the State of Bath, who was present at this discussion, now came forward to declare his conviction that these arguments, though not without plausibility, were entirely unsound, and his confidence that he should be able to establish this to the satisfaction of the whole party; but he proposed to defer giving his reasons till they should have viewed a spot in his neighbourhood, curious and interesting on many accounts, and closely and historically connected with the subject under discussion.

This was the celebrated Mount Peril (already alluded to), in the immediate vicinity of the city of Bath. The invitation was accepted; and the travellers shortly after set out on their excursion to visit this mountain. It plainly appears to be an extinct volcano. The settlers found it regarded with superstitious awe by the natives, who had among them a tradition of smoke having been seen at times to issue from it, and who regarded it as the habitation of certain malignant deities, of a similar character to the Pèlè venerated in the island of Hawaii (Owhyhee). The medicinal warm springs flowing from the foot of it gave occasion to the fixing of the city of Bath (thence so named) in the neighbourhood. It is one of the oldest states, the warm baths having early acquired such repute as to be highly attractive.

The circumstance which gave rise to the appellation of Mount Peril was the existence of certain caverns and fissures on one of its sides, emitting at times noxious vapours, which had more than once proved fatal to those who had incautiously ventured too near them. These were reputed by the natives to be the abode of evil spirits, destructive to such as approached them: and in the etymological sense of the word spirit (*spiritus*, blast) this might be said to be literally true; for our travellers soon ascertained that the danger arose from a deleterious gas, the same that in coalpits is called the choke-damp, found also in the celebrated "Grotto del Cane" in Italy, named and long celebrated for the cruel experiments practised on dogs for the gratification of travellers. This gas, now well known to every smatterer in chemistry as the carbonic acid gas, so poisonous when received into the lungs, issues forth, it should seem, in irregular blasts from these caverns, so as to render them more dangerous of approach at some times than at others; so that many persons have passed with impunity spots which have at different times affected others with alarming or even fatal suffocation.

The cavern which the travellers inspected the most closely is situated at the foot of a perpendicular cliff, about fifty feet in height, from the top of which the mouth may be seen very distinctly and with perfect safety; the gas being, as is well known, so much heavier than common air that there is no danger of its rising even near so high as the top of the cliff. The visitors tried the experiment of letting down by a rope, with a chain at the lower end of it, a little iron grating brought for the purpose, containing (as a humane substitute for a living dog) splinters of dry wood set on fire, which being lowered when in a full blaze into the cavern's mouth, were suddenly and completely extinguished. This cavern was easily accessible from below, as it opened a kind of terrace of nearly level ground, called "the Ordeal Path;" but though many persons had passed it with impunity, it was considered too hazardous an experiment to be wantonly risked.

# CHAPTER IV

*Superstitious Notions.—Abolition of Duelling.—Interference of Providence.—Challenge to the Ordeal.—The Trial.—Conviction of the Offender.—Uncertainty of the Ordeal.—Ineffectual Prohibition.—Check against Slander.—Exclusion from Society.—Absurd Alternative.—Personal Courage.—Imputation of Cowardice.—Public Opinion.—War between Nations.—Challenges.—Fear of Disgrace.*

Mr. Adamson afterwards proceeded to relate the circumstances connected with the cavern. Many superstitious notions, it seems, and much tendency to give credit to tales of supernatural mystery had been brought from Europe by several of the original settlers, trained as they had been in the then prevailing credulity, and many of them tinctured with fanaticism. It is not to be wondered therefore, that, ignorant as they were of physical phenomena, several should have given more or less credit to the reports of the natives respecting evil demons dwelling in these caverns; the dangerous nature of them having been proved in some instances by fatal experience.

The employment of one of them for the purpose of an ordeal originated long after. "It ought in the first place to be acknowledged," said Mr. Adamson, "that the barbarian institution of duels did exist among us, though now long since exploded."

They were not of common occurrence; but he added that his father distinctly remembered as a boy the final abolition of the practice, in the manner about to be related. The duel was regarded—and such is well known to have been its original design—as a kind of ordeal, as a solemn appeal to Heaven, which it was supposed would not fail to interfere in support of the rightful combatant.

And here Mr. Sibthorpe had the candour to interpose a remark, that, though *duels* have long since ceased to be considered in that light, the general principle is very far from being exploded among a large proportion of our own countrymen, who frequently apply the terms "providential," and even "miraculous," to the detection of murderers; the frustration of schemes of injustice; the escape of pious men from dangers of shipwreck or fire, &c. and who speak of pestilential diseases, conflagrations, and other fatal accidents, as judgments from Heaven on the sufferers; evidently referring to a supposed special interference of Providence to allot temporal successes or adversities according to the deserts of the parties; and often setting down as little better than an atheist any one who questions such a doctrine.

"Now," said he, "if it be admitted that there is a special and extraordinary interference of Providence for the immediate temporal punishment of the wicked, and for the securing of success to a righteous cause, there seems no reason why this should not be looked for in the case of a judicial combat. Our ancestors were at least as wise as we, and more consistent, if we deride or reprobate the idea of a special interposition of Providence in the case of a single combat, while we look for it in all *other* cases. And you well know," added he to Mr. Jones, "how strongly the doctrine I allude to is set forth in newspapers—in magazines—in publications of various descriptions, and, not least, in the nursery-books which are first put into the hands of children."

This could not be denied. "Well, such," continued Mr. Adamson, "had been our belief as well as yours. But while the trial by single combat was retained under an altered character, the other kinds of ordeal—such as the hot ploughshare, &c. to which women, as well as men, had in former times been exposed—fell completely into desuetude."

Among the Southlanders the institution was, by an accidental circumstance, reintroduced. It seems that a woman, named Margaret Brucker, had been grossly defamed by a neighbour, and being highly indignant at the imputations cast on her virtue, and conscious of perfect innocence, she appealed to the judgment of Heaven, and challenged her accuser to accompany her publicly along the mountain side, by what was afterwards called the 'Ordeal Path,' to pass by the goblin cavern, the one viewed by our travellers. She professed her full confidence that her innocence would protect her from the demons residing there, and that the false accusation would be visited by a divine judgment on her who had devised it. Margaret appears to have been a perfectly sincere enthusiast, and to have possessed that fervid eloquence which is the result of genuine strong feeling. This, together with youth, beauty, and the sympathy excited by her distress of mind, operated so strongly on the superstitious feelings of the people that they vehemently seconded her proposal; and the woman who had accused her dared not refuse the trial.

The parties accordingly set forth, attended by a great concourse of eager spectators, who ranged themselves on the edge of the cliff overhanging the cavern in breathless expectation of the results. The magistrates had only ventured to exert their authority so far as to require that ropes should be let down from the top of the cliff, and secured by straps to the body of each of the women, so that in case of danger they might be safely drawn up.

Margaret, with a firm and undaunted step, walked unhurt close along the mouth of the cavern. Her companion, who had been observed to become pale and agitated as they approached the scene of trial, sank down insensible at the entrance of the cavern. The mingled shouts of wonder, alarm, horror, and exultation proceeding from the spectators of this complete fulfilment of the prophecy may easily be imagined. The fainting victim was drawn up by the rope to the top of the cliff, to all appearance dead. By sprinkling her with water, however, she gradually revived; and on being restored to her senses and speech, confessed, with much awe and contrition, the entire falsity of the stories she had circulated, and which she had fabricated through jealousy. She acknowledged, and no doubt fully believed, that she had been struck down by the demon of the goblin cavern as a just judgment on her calumny. Of course Margaret Brucker was venerated as little less than a prophetess, and the ordeal rose into high and general repute.

Several, indeed, of the more sagacious entertained at the time the opinion which it would then have been most discreditable to avow, but which has long since become universal, that the one party escaped unhurt because she walked erect across the opening of the cavern, the noxious gas being so heavy that its influence does not usually extend much more than one or two feet above the surface of the ground; and that the other, through the agitation of conscious guilt and superstitious terror, either turned giddy, or stumbled over a stone, and falling down, was immediately exposed to the full current of the vapour. This is agreeable to what is found to take place in the celebrated Grotto del Cane, which is entered with impunity by men, but is fatal to a dog (whose head is so much nearer to the ground) if the poor beast is compelled to remain over one of the fissures from which the gas issues.

The ordeal, however, was a very uncertain one, from the variations occurring in the quantity of vapour emitted. Sometimes both parties were suffocated, and oftener both escaped unhurt; and in some instances, as might have been expected, it happened that a person whose character had been cleared by the ordeal, was afterwards, by circumstances subsequently brought to light, proved, or violently suspected, to have been guilty.

Instances of this kind, in conjunction with the advancement of intellectual culture, gradually weakened, in progress of time, the belief in the supernatural character of the ordeal. It was, however, for a long time, frequently appealed to, both by women and men, from all the states; and, in spite of laws which were passed, but which it was found impossible fully to enforce, prohibiting any such trial, and denouncing as murder the offence of being accessary to any one's exposure to it in case of a fatal result,—the custom still received the sanction of many who disavowed all belief of miraculous interference in the case of such trials.

"They defended," said Mr. Adamson, "by nearly the same arguments as I have lately heard from you, both duels, such as you apply the name to, and these which were always very justly regarded as a kind of duel; since there is no essential difference between calling on your adversary to stand a pistol-shot or a poisonous blast. It was conducive, they contended, to the preservation of good manners, and of a high and delicate sense of honour in both sexes, that a man should be restrained from ungentlemanly behaviour, and from lightly taxing another with it, by the apprehension of personal danger; and that female purity should be guarded in like manner. 'It is,' they said, 'a useful additional check against lying, for instance, and against rashly charging another with being a liar, to reflect on the probable consequence of being called on to face the sword or pistol, or the goblin cavern of Mount Peril. And it is but fair, that a woman also should recollect that levity of conduct, or wanton slander, may occasion her to be required to undergo a similar danger.' There were not wanting many who reprobated this doctrine, and urged such arguments on the other side respecting the wickedness and the absurdity of the custom as we have lately heard from Mr. Jones. But they were urged with as little practical effect as they appear to have had among you. At length, several persons of the higher classes, and remarkable for correctness of life, refinement of manners, and cultivated understanding, formed themselves into an association and declared strenuous war against every kind of duel, including, as has been said, under that name the ordeal of the cavern, which they contended against on entirely new grounds.

"They did not confine themselves to such topics as had been before, again and again, urged without effect; but maintained that the practice tended to defeat the very end proposed, and to lower (instead of raising, as was pretended) the tone of manners in the society. 'If,' they said, 'there were no such custom, then, any one, whether man or woman, who transgressed the rules which public opinion had sanctioned in the circle of society in which he or she moved, would at once be excluded from that circle. And the apprehension of this exclusion, of thus losing caste, and being sent to Coventry, which is the ultimate penalty that such a society can inflict for a breach of its rules, would be the best preventive of any violation of them,—the best preservative of the tone of the society, that it is possible to attain. If, under such a system, any one insulted another, he would be regarded as an ill-mannered brute, and excluded from good company: a woman who displayed levity of conduct would be at once excluded from reputable society: any one, man or woman, who should bring rash imputations against a neighbour, would be shunned as a slanderer: and so of the rest. But under the system of duelling, society offers an *alternative*; the only effect of which, as far as it operates, is unmixed evil. Instead of saying, absolutely, you must abstain from brutal insolence of demeanour, on pain of being excluded from our circle, it says, you must *either* abstain from insolence, *or* be ready to expose your life; instead of requiring a woman to abstain from levity of conduct, and defamatory language, on pain of forfeiting the countenance of respectable people, it proposes the alternative of *either* observing those rules, *or* the being prepared to encounter the ordeal; and the result is, that those who possess personal intrepidity will often be enabled to transgress with impunity those rules of good society, which the duelling system professes to enforce. Nay more; the system tends to invest with a certain degree of dignity, arising from our admiration of personal courage, such conduct as would otherwise excite only unmitigated abhorrence and contempt. An insolent man, for instance, if by his insolence he braved no danger but that of expulsion from good company, would be simply despised: but since he also, under the other system, braves the danger of death, he obtains some degree of honour for his intrepidity. And though some may be deterred from such conduct by the fear of a challenge, others, on the contrary, may be encouraged to it, by a desire of displaying valour; especially if they have reason to think, from what they know of the other party, that a challenge will *not* ensue, and that they shall enjoy their triumph unmolested.

"'Moreover, the magnitude of the injuries which one person actually can do to another is infinitely enhanced by the system of duels, because every affront offered is thus made to carry with it an imputation on one's personal courage, which can only be wiped out by the exposure of life. If, for instance, I am a man of uniform and scrupulous veracity, and some ill-mannered ruffian gives me the lie, then, supposing duels unknown, the attack recoils entirely on the assailant. He is incapable of proving his charge—my life refutes it,—and the only result is that *he*, not I, is set down as a liar, for having falsely called me a liar. But under the other system, I must go out and expose my life, or else I am disgraced—disgraced, not as a *liar* (for *that* imputation, perhaps, is disbelieved after all), but as a *coward*, for not daring to risk my life in defence of my honour. And thus a person, who otherwise might have been incapable of doing me any serious hurt at all, has it in his power to propose to me at his pleasure the alternative of hazard to my life and violence to my conscience, or ignominy. A venom is thus added to the sting of the most contemptible insect.

"'So much,' said they, 'for the protection thus provided for us against injuries the most painful to the feelings! Great part of the disgrace attaching to the authors of such injuries is removed; the injuries are probably rather increased than diminished in frequency; and in the pain they inflict, they are undoubtedly aggravated tenfold.' With regard to the supposed necessity for a person's thus vindicating his own honour in certain cases, on the ground that the parties have no common authority to appeal to, this they flatly denied. The public opinion of the society they belong to, *is* that common authority. And that it is so, and is competent to decide effectually, is proved, they urged, by the very existence of duelling; for the duel itself is enforced by nothing else but public opinion. I am obliged, it is said, to challenge a man who has affronted me, because there is no authority to appeal to that will compel him to redress the injury. But what, then, compels him to *accept* the challenge? Nothing, but the knowledge that if he refused it, society would reject him as disgraced. Then, why should not society at once pronounce on him this sentence of disgrace for the affront itself, unless he makes a satisfactory submission? If he defies public opinion, and does not care for disgrace, he need not accept the challenge: if he does care for public opinion, then let the disgrace attach at once to the offering of the affront, instead of to the refusal of the challenge. It is manifest that those who have the power to propose the alternative, of either suffering disgrace or fighting, must have the power to discard the latter part of the alternative. Let society, therefore, but do its duty, and it is plain that it may, by a proper exertion of the power which it has, and which it actually exercises even now, restrain, and restrain much more effectually, without duelling, the very evils which duelling professes to remedy.

"As for the case of war between independent states, this," observed Mr. Adamson, "by the way, is by no means a parallel to that of private duels. One nation does not *send a challenge* to another; because, as the parties really have no common authority to refer to, the aggressors would of course decline the challenge, and *would* prefer enjoying unmolested the fruits of their injustice. The nation, therefore, which considers itself aggrieved has no other remedy than, after complaining and demanding redress in vain, to declare war, levy troops, and commence hostilities against its opponents without waiting for their consent; and this procedure would be parallel to the case of duels only, if these were quite of a different character from what they are. If it were customary for a man who had received an affront to declare *war* against his neighbour, arm himself, and *proceed to attack* him without asking his consent, this would correspond to a war between two states. But a *challenge* is quite a different thing; it is an invitation which a man may either accept or decline, to meet at a time and place settled by mutual agreement, where the parties, by common consent, expose themselves to a certain specified risk. Generally, the challenge is both sent and accepted, not from motives of revenge, but from fear of public censure: but universally, the party challenged might refuse it if he were willing to brave public censure.

"So far, therefore, is a duel from being a mode of repelling injury, which a man is driven to resort to through the want of any common authority to appeal to, that, on the contrary, every duel actually rests on a tacit appeal to such an authority—viz. to public opinion; since no one could compel another to afford him the satisfaction sought except through the influence of the fear of disgrace, the other being at liberty to refuse the challenge if he dares to set public opinion at defiance. Every duel, therefore, whether actually taking place, or merely talked of and threatened, is itself a complete disproof of the plea on *which* duels are justified."

# CHAPTER V

*Female Honour.—Agreement among Women.—Penalty of Exclusion.—Law of Honour.—False Dignity.—New Penalty.—Compact against Duelling.—Ruffians and Calumniators.—Association against Duelling.—Court of Honour.—Abolition of Duelling.*

"That public opinion, if rightly directed, is capable," continued Mr. Adamson, "of completely affecting the desired object without the duel, even better than with it, which is what we of the present day are so happy as to know by experience, these reformers anticipated partly from the enforcement among ladies of the laws of female honour before that absurd ordeal had been instituted. Women moving in circles of good society had kept up its character, it was observed, at least as well before the ordeal came into use, and quite as well as men of a corresponding class maintained the laws of masculine honour; and this was effected simply by a tacit agreement among women of character not to associate with any woman who was known to have violated these rules. 'If, therefore,' said they, 'ladies will return to this system, and gentlemen will adopt a corresponding one, the rules of good society, whatever they may be that it thinks fit to impose, will be enforced by the simple expedient of denouncing exclusion against the violators of them, absolutely, and without offering the alternative of a duel.'

"It was remarked, indeed, by some of you," said Mr. Adamson, "that in Europe the ladies, and also some other classes of persons who are exempted from the liability to a duel, are apt to avail themselves of this exemption by a less scrupulous adherence to truth and to courtesy of language, or by throwing such aspersions on their neighbours as would involve in personal danger those not so privileged; and such instances of falsehood, insolence, and calumny were attributed by some of you to the absence of the salutary check of the duel.

"As to the precise state of the fact, indeed, you appeared not to be quite agreed: but admitting the most unfavourable representation to be true, you may perceive, even from what comes under your own experience, without resorting to ours, that the inference drawn is not correct; for it appears by your own account that the English women, of the higher classes at least, though all kinds of duel are unknown among them, yet keep up the character of their society in respect of female purity. And, as this is effected through the direct influence of public opinion,—by simply enforcing the penalty of exclusion on any female of blemished reputation,—it is evident that if in respect of veracity, integrity, or any other point, they fall short of what is required of gentlemen, this must arise from the standard of *honour* being different in the two sexes. I collect that among you the character of 'an honest woman' does not coincide with that of 'an honest man,'—and that even the word 'virtue' has a somewhat different signification in reference to women and to men. It cannot be therefore that public opinion is insufficient to enforce the laws of honour without the intervention of duels, since modest women do succeed in maintaining the purity of the society in which they move; but the laws of honour are themselves not the same among ladies and among gentlemen. The fact is, few persons, either men or women, will venture to incur infamy; and *that* is the penalty *which* society may denounce against the violation of its rules, be those rules what they may. Let society determine what shall be the point of honour for each sex, or class of persons, or for all, and denounce the penalty of exclusion against such as violate its rules; and that those rules will be generally observed, without the intervention of duelling, is proved by the very circumstance that women enforce their own law of honour as successfully as men do theirs!

"By acting on these principles," continued Mr. Adamson, "you would have the additional advantage of imposing a restraint on those females, and others, who, you complain, are disposed to take advantage of their exemption from danger of a challenge by indulging in defamatory or insolent language, &c.; for, as I just now observed, conduct of this kind is regarded among you with somewhat the less of unmixed disgust and contempt, from the very circumstance that among laymen of a certain station it may lead to a duel. It is considered as in some degree a mark of 'spirit.' The courage which braves death, even when disapproved as a brutal kind of courage, yet shelters its possessor from the last extreme of ignominy. Now, though the degree of false dignity with which insolent behaviour is thus invested *ought* certainly to be at least confined to those who actually do run a risk in displaying it,—though women and clergymen, for instance, since they run no risk, and consequently display no courage by such behaviour as would expose a layman to personal danger, should properly be considered base as well as unmannerly when they are guilty of it,—yet this distinction is one which we cannot expect will be carefully kept in view and uniformly observed. A kind of association of ideas is created in people's minds between what is called 'spirited behaviour,' 'strong language,' &c. and 'manly boldness;' and this association continues to affect their judgment even in cases where no boldness is really displayed, because no danger is encountered. Thus, such conduct, in a woman for instance, or in a clergyman, as would otherwise incur unmixed contempt, is likely to be, if not altogether honoured or approved, at least in some degree tolerated.

"But let the system be changed, and the tone of manners in *all* classes would be raised. When duels are unheard of, such offences as are now regarded with a mitigated disapprobation on account of the personal intrepidity which they are supposed sometimes to imply in the offenders, would become the subject of unmixed disgust; the only danger braved being that of the disesteem of reputable people. And *this* kind of penalty extending to *all* classes and both sexes alike, (at least among the gentry,) would of course tend to restrain all of them alike within the rules of honour and politeness. There may be some reason why, among you, a woman should not be called out to *fight*; but there could be none, why she should not incur, as well as a gentleman, the penalty, when that was the *sole* penalty for both sexes alike, of *exclusion* from good society if she transgressed its rules: a penalty which in fact actually *is* enforced, with unrelenting strictness, for a violation of the rules of what is now accounted feminine honour.

"Such nearly," continued Mr. Adamson, "was the train of argument, as far as applicable to the then-existing condition of society among us, which was strenuously urged, and assiduously circulated by the association against duels which I have alluded to. The novelty of the arguments contributed, along with their intrinsic force, and the high character of those who urged them, to excite a general and serious attention; and the judicious course pursued by the authors of the undertaking secured them ultimate success. The members of the association bound themselves, by a solemn compact with each other, never to give or accept a challenge to any kind of duel, whether by the ordeal, or by single combat; never to behave in such a manner as might otherwise have afforded occasion for a duel; and not to countenance or receive into their society any one who should violate either of the above rules. In cases of personal assault, they were at liberty to defend themselves by force on the spot; but not to seek any subsequent satisfaction, except by an appeal to the laws, and by agreeing to shun the society of the offender as of a ruffian. They were to defend themselves against slander by *living it down*—by giving the false accuser the lie in their conduct; but they were to seek no other redress (unless they thought fit to bring a legal action for defamation) than by excluding calumniators from their society.

"And the same in respect of rude and insolent language: into *their* society, no daring ruffian, however expert in snuffing a candle with a bullet, could, as formerly, *fight* his way, by inducing those who really thought him no fit company for gentlemen, by a tacit appeal to their personal fears to admit him as an associate; each inwardly wishing all the while that one of the others would undertake the perilous task of tying the bell round his neck. Every such person, and every one in any way of exceptionable character, was under the ban of hopeless exclusion. It was useless to challenge the excluders, since they had proclaimed that they would not fight. From personal violence they appealed to the law: insolent vituperation was unavailing; since being directed against men who had abjured duels, it was understood to imply no personal risk, and consequently to give no proof of courage. From well-founded accusations, their blameless life and decorous behaviour secured them; unfounded charges only proclaimed the authors of them to be themselves liars.

"Very early in the history of this association, a question arose among its members, on the decision of which, probably, their final success turned. It was at first designed that they should continue formally to enrol as members as many unexceptionable persons as could be induced to join their society. Some of their number, however, objected that this would be likely to impede their progress in the reformation they were aiming at. A jealousy, they said, would be likely to arise in the minds of some persons against the pretensions, real or supposed, of an association of which they were not themselves the founders or leaders. They would therefore be apt perversely to refuse joining it, as disdaining to follow in the wake of others; and would then set about justifying their conduct by exciting suspicion and organizing opposition, as against a party combining to set up themselves as arbiters of good manners,—guides to the rest of the world,—a self-constituted tribunal, &c.

"These representations prevailed; and a resolution was adopted, and publicly announced, (accompanied with a frank statement of the reasons for it,) not to admit formally from thenceforth any more persons as members, except such as might have been actually engaged in a duel, and were desirous of thus solemnly and publicly proclaiming their renunciation of a practice to which they had thus once lent their countenance. But all other persons of respectable character, it was declared, should be thenceforth regarded as virtually members of the association, without any formal admission or engagement, so long as they should continue in practice to comply with the fundamental rules of the society, by abstaining from duels, and from everything calculated to provoke a challenge, and by shunning the company of those who acted otherwise. If any should in practice violate these regulations, or should openly proclaim his determination not to adhere to them, then, and then only, he was to be regarded as excluded from the number of the associates.

"In all cases of dispute arising between one gentleman or lady and another, the cause was to be referred to the decision, not of any self-appointed tribunal, nor of any formally-elected court of honour (either of which might have furnished occasion for jealousy), but of a committee of the neighbours meeting for the purpose, with the stipulation only that they should be persons received in good society and adverse to duelling. Of such persons, each of the parties chooses (for the custom was adopted, and still exists among us,) one or two of his acquaintance,—each of whom again names two or three others as assessors,—and the judges thus nominated privately hear and try the cause, calling in, in case of much difficulty or disagreement, the assistance of others. It is seldom that the parties do not readily acquiesce in the decision; and the public in general are, as you may suppose, fully prepared to think that this must be at least more likely to approach to a right judgment than a pistol-ball or a blast of choke-damp.

"In this way it was that the custom of duels gradually, and not very slowly, went out of fashion among us. It has been wholly extinct for more than a century; for my father, who, as I mentioned just now, remembered as a boy the final prevalence of this reform, was born nearly one hundred and thirty years ago.

"If the same reform," he added, "is not effected by the gentry of Europe, when they have only to *will* that it should be so, their claims to a high degree of civilization and refinement (to say nothing of humanity or morality) can hardly be admitted. For example, as it is, any one who offers an affront to another, and on being challenged refuses to fight, is excluded from the pale of good society; unless it be a woman—a clergyman—a quaker—a person bound over to keep the peace, under the penalty of forfeiting a sum of money—(a curious exemption this!)—or belonging to some other description of privileged persons. All you have to do is to resolve that the *offering* of the affront shall place any person under the same ban as he is now placed under for refusing, after being challenged for the affront, to fight. Lay down this rule; and let there be *no exemptions* on the ground of sex, profession, or any other plea whatever, and the object is accomplished."

# CHAPTER VI

*Rough Notes.—Public Entertainments.—Dancing.—Grotesque Dance.—Throwing the Spear.—Female Dress.—Decorations.—Ear-rings.—Wedding-rings.—Anomalous Costume.*

The rough notes taken down by the several members of the exploring party are, of course, not arranged in the order of the subjects, but are merely memoranda written on the spot from time to time according as the knowledge was obtained, or the observations made; and in the selections here laid before the reader, it has been thought best not to attempt any systematic arrangement, but to present them in their original miscellaneous form.

While the travellers were at Bath,—which is a city rather distinguished, like its namesake in England and in Germany, for gaiety, as being a place of resort to strangers on account of the mineral waters,—they were invited to several public entertainments of various kinds, and of different degrees of solemnity and splendour. One lady with whom, among others, they were conversing on the subject of one of these which they were about to attend, on being asked, among other inquiries, whether a ball possessed as much attraction for young people as, they told her, it does in Europe, replied in the affirmative; though, for her own part, she said, she liked archery better; but different young people, said she, differ, you know, in their tastes in respect of amusements.

When the gay party had been assembled,—which was on a lawn of considerable extent, partially shaded with some fine mimosa and eucalyptus (gum-tree), under whose shade tents were erected,—the travellers witnessed with much interest the several diversions that were going on; and, among others, their notice was called by the lady with whom they had been conversing the day before to several "games of ball" of various kinds that were going on; some played by gentlemen alone, some by ladies, and some by both together; and many of them bearing more or less resemblance to the English games of cricket, bowls, trap-ball, tennis, billiards, &c. as well as to others which are common enough among children in England, but quite unknown among adults.

The travellers laughed heartily (as the ladies did also, on receiving an explanation) at the mutual mistake they had made about balls: but, on making more particular inquiries about dancing, they learned that this was an amusement confined to children; scarcely any ever joining in that sport except those under thirteen or fourteen years old, and any lively and good-humoured friend of the children, who joined their game for their amusement. The sport was in fact "playing at being savages," the dances consisting in a ludicrous imitation of those of the aborigines. These, it is well known, are much given to dancing, in which they display considerable ingenuity as well as agility and good ear; and their dances are not merely a recreation, but are also mixed up with their most important institutions and transactions, being performed with much solemnity at their "corrobories," or grand meetings, for the purpose of deliberating on affairs of state, and performing certain superstitious rites of divination.

A group of romping boys and girls, who were at play in one corner of the field, were accordingly requested to exhibit to the strangers the spectacle of a dance; and some of the most forward and lively of the boys entered into the proposal with much glee. Two of the party took on themselves, by general consent, the arrangement and direction of the whole, and seemed to officiate as masters of the ceremonies, or, as they called themselves, "Corrobory chiefs." They were, it seems, visitors from one of the back-settlements, and had had frequent opportunities of witnessing the native dances. The sport partook somewhat of the nature of a masquerade; some whimsical changes being made in the costume of the dancers, in order to give the livelier representation of the strange originals. Much merriment took place, and many curious feats of grotesque agility were displayed, to the great diversion both of the juvenile performers and the bystanders. This sport was followed by the throwing of the spear, after the manner of the natives; an art in which many of the Southlanders are very expert, especially those who live on the margins of the lakes, where the striking of fish is a favourite diversion, as the salmon-spearing is in some parts of Scotland. The throwing of the spear at a mark, however, and also archery, are games not confined, as dancing is, to children.

The Southlanders expressed surprise that adult Europeans, even of the higher classes, should retain the amusement of dancing, "like the savages;" an amusement which seemed to them, from habit, as childish as many of their sports, on the other hand, had appeared to their visitors. Both parties were somewhat at a loss to explain to each other the grounds of their respective notions as to what was or was not puerile. "There is no disputing," said one of the most intelligent of their hosts, "about tastes; but in many points, I believe, ours are to be accounted for by that early and deep-seated association in our minds, which you have in many instances noticed, between certain practices or habits and savage life. You have remarked several times how frequently the phrase is in our mouths, that to do so and so is 'like the savages;' and this may perhaps account for the ridiculous appearance which, as you perceive, one of your balls, as you call them, would have in our eyes."

The sentiment above alluded to was manifested in several conversations (occurring at various places, and noticed from time to time in the memorandum-books of the travellers,) on the subject of dress, especially female dress; respecting which the ladies showed themselves, as was to be expected, inquisitive and communicative. They generally expressed their wonder, when the female costume of England was described, that people pretending to be so civilized should expose so much *bare flesh,* "like the savages." The habit of dressing, or rather, as they said, of undressing, so as to display naked shoulders, bosoms, and arms, struck them more as barbarian than as indelicate; they themselves,—though their clothing is usually thin, on account of the general warmth of the climate,—leave no part of the body uncovered, except the face and hands. They inquired whether the European ladies coat themselves with grease, mixed up with ochre or other paint, as the savages do, by way of protection to the unclothed parts from scorching sun, piercing winds, and the bites of mosquitoes; also, whether they practised the tattooing, which is an essential part of aboriginal finery.

They inquired also whether English ladies did not suffer in their health from the great and sudden *changes,* from covering to exposure, of many parts of the body between morning and evening dresses; and also whether many of them did not become diseased or deformed by the violence with which they appeared to squeeze their waists. Wilkins, the servant, it seems, had chanced to bring with him a lady's almanac, containing plates of "female costume," which excited great interest, wonder, and diversion among the Southlanders. Some imagined at first, among other mistakes, that the ladies were represented as taking precautions against drowning, by fastening, as the Southlanders sometimes do, large bladders to their arms.

They expressed hardly less wonder on learning that English ladies are accustomed, "like the savages," to wear feathers, necklaces, and other ornaments, and even to make incisions in their flesh for the purpose of inserting them. They asked whether, in addition to ear-rings, they wore nose-rings, and the ornament so general among the New-Hollanders, called humorously by the English sailors the "spritsail-yard;" viz. the leg-bone of a bird thrust through the middle cartilage of the nose.

The travellers observed, in reply, that the Southlanders, especially the females, seemed to have no scruples on the subject of ornamental dress and furniture, as they had much that was both handsome and costly. "That is true," said one of the party; "and though there are many differences of opinion on the subject, and some indulge in a degree of attention to ornament which is regarded by others as excessive, the total condemnation of all regard to decoration is by no means common. The church, indeed, of the Kernhuters—of which I learn from you there is a considerable and valuable remnant in Europe—have adopted, for nearly two centuries, some very strict regulations on this head; among others, they make it a point of discipline to use no dyes. Their shoes and boots are brown, of the natural colour of the leather; their coats grey, being made of a mixture of black wool and white, as it comes from the sheep; and their hats of the natural colour of the opossum and kangaroo: but these are exceptions. The point *agreed on* among us, and in which our difference from you gave rise to the wonder you heard expressed, is this,—that it is barbarian to wear anything *for the sake* of ornament, and which answers no purpose but that of decoration. Of this description are feathers, which were worn by our ancestors of both sexes, but which I understand from you are now confined to women, and to military men when in uniform. So, also, are necklaces, rings, and, above all, ear-rings. It strikes us as peculiarly barbarian to bore holes in the flesh for the purpose of sticking in ornaments. It may be a prejudice, but it is at least an ancient one; for the Greeks, though I believe their women wore ear-rings,—and it is to be observed that they regarded women as a very inferior order of beings, and rather as toys, or as domestic drudges, than as civilized and rational companions,—considered ear-rings worn by men as a decisive mark of barbarism. You may find, in Xenophon's Anabasis, one of the captains of companies, who had given some cowardly advice, reproached as uttering sentiments unworthy of a Greek; on which some one exclaimed 'He is no Greek! *his ears are bored*:' and this being ascertained by inspection, he was on this evidence at once pronounced a barbarian, and as such reduced to the ranks.

"You have observed," continued he, "among us handsome and costly gold brooches and buckles, buttons made of jewels, embroidered garments, inlaid tables, and other such ornamental articles; but you will see no article that is *merely* an ornament. A gold brooch or button served as a fastening, not better indeed, but as well, as an iron or brass one. Its *beauty* is superfluous, but it is not *itself* superfluous, and destitute of all ostensible use. So, also, a silver goblet serves to drink out of, and an embroidered gown to cover one, no less than plain ones. The robes, caps, and thrones of our higher magistrates are, as you have seen, in some instances very highly decorated;

but they have an ostensible use, as coverings and seats. We have no necklaces, plumes, or rings; and have indeed carried so far this distinction, which probably to you seems fanciful, that we have even laid aside the ancient usage of the wedding ring, and, as you must have observed, mark the distinction between the married and single by the dress. By the bye," he added, "the ring, which you speak of as having a use in distinguishing a married *woman*, is confined, I perceive, to the *wife*; a married *man* not having, as among us, any distinctive mark."

Mr. Sibthorpe here remarked, that though any practice to which we are not accustomed does usually appear to us fanciful, yet it occurred to him—what had never struck him before—that no *mere* ornament is commonly worn by *men* of the present age in Europe; a few, indeed, wear rings, but not the majority; nor is it any requisition of fashion. Stars, ribbons, crowns, &c. are worn by men as marks of certain rank or office; but the feathers, chains, shoulder-knots, and ruffles, which our forefathers wore as a part of fashionable dress, are obsolete. Man is now so far conformed to the ancient definition as to be "a biped without *feathers*;" women, on the contrary, are so far, according to the Southlanders, in the rear of advancing civilization as still to wear ornaments, like the savages.

He remarked also another point of coincidence between European women on the one side, and European men and the Southlanders of both sexes on the other; the latter, he observed, were always dressed *alike on both sides*, so that if one imagined one of them split into halves, the two would *match*, like a pair of gloves; among European ladies, on the contrary, most of the many great variations of fashion agree in making some difference between the two sides; there is usually an obliquity in the head-gear, or a bow, a feather, or a bunch of flowers, stuck on one side, without a corresponding one on the other.

# CHAPTER VII

*Forms of Government.—Senatorial Regulations.—Speakers.—Peculiar Debate.—Fundamental Laws.—Unwise Legislators.—Timely Improvements.—Legislative Problem.—Legislative Expedient.—Error in Government.—Division of Laws.—Repeal of Fundamental Laws.—Guard against Precipitancy.—Laws of Treason.—Mature Deliberation.—National Will.*

All the states, which, as has been mentioned above, are eleven in number, differ more or less from each other in their form of government, but are alike in all the most important and fundamental principles adopted; several of which are strangely at variance with everything that is to be found in the northern hemisphere. Seven out of the eleven states are denominated kingdoms: but of these, four only are under an hereditary royalty; the other three being, as far as the travellers could ascertain, rather of the character of republics than of strictly regal governments; but retaining the title of King to denote the chief magistrate for the time being, somewhat corresponding to the Athenian archon, Roman consul, or American president. There are four other states also which are, in name as well as in substance, republics. But these differences are greater in appearance than in reality; the kingdoms which are the most strictly so called, being by no means under an unlimited monarchy.

Many of the particulars respecting the constitutions and laws of the several states the travellers were of course, during their short stay, unable to collect, except very slightly and imperfectly. From those which they did collect, and ascertain with sufficient certainty, we shall select such as are likely to be the most interesting, from their dissimilarity to European institutions.

It was in the state of Atroloria,—so called from the lake of the same name[1] within its territory,—which the travellers first reached, that they had the earliest opportunity of witnessing debates in their senate. They afterwards, on several occasions, attended the legislative assemblies in other places. The circumstance which in the first instance most attracted, by its novelty to them, the attention of the visitors, was one which they found on inquiry was common to all the states in their deliberative assemblies; being a regulation originally established by Müller, and afterwards, from its tried advantage and convenience, continued universally and uninterruptedly. It was this, that no member was allowed to *speak* and to *vote* on the same question, but each had his choice between the two. The proceedings, accordingly, bore some resemblance to those of a court of justice in civil causes; the speakers corresponding to the pleaders who address the court,—the voters, to the jury, who give the verdict. The difference is, that each member has it left to his choice which character he will take. Any member wishing to address the house, quits his seat and places himself in front of the chair of the moderator,—answering to the speaker or chairman; and when he has spoken, seats himself, not in his former place, but, with a view to prevent mistake or confusion, on a bench appropriated to the purpose, and thence called the speakers' bench; or he is at liberty to leave the assembly if he thinks fit. When the question has been put to the vote and decided, and a fresh question is coming on, he resumes his original seat. Certain public functionaries, who are not members, have a seat by right on the speakers' bench, and are at liberty to address the house (though they have no vote) when there is any reference to the business of their own peculiar departments.

1. The lake was so called by the early settlers; doubtless from the same cause which led to the name of our own colony in Western Australia.

Whether owing to this circumstance, or to any other, the debates were observed to be shorter, and the speakers much fewer, than is usual in European assemblies. They seldom exceeded two or three on each side.

The travellers observed that the speakers rarely used even the smallest degree of action, but usually kept themselves remarkably still while speaking. This, it appears, was one of the results of that general and deep-rooted association already alluded to. In the course of conversation on this subject, the Southlanders, it appeared, considered it as something uncivilized to use either vociferation or gesticulation in speaking, "as the savages do." They even accounted the refined Athenians and Romans of old as little better than half-reclaimed barbarians in this respect, because they would not attend to an orator unless he stamped and shouted, and brandished his arms about, as if he were speaking to a pack of hounds, instead of to an assembly of rational beings.

The travellers were so fortunate as to witness on one occasion a debate of a peculiar kind, which is of rare occurrence, and which served to throw light on the whole system of legislature of this singular people. It occurred in the kingdom of Nether-London, one of the most ancient and populous of all the states. They found a considerable excitement and bustle prevailing, though all was orderly and decorous, on account of a summons issued (in our phraseology, "a call of the house") to the members of their assembly, called in that state the parliament, to deliberate on the question of removing a *fundamental law*. The particular law then in question was, they found, like the Salic law of the French, one which confined the succession to the throne to males. But a further inquiry let them into the knowledge of matter far more curious and interesting,—the general principle of "fundamental laws," which materially affects the whole of the system of legislature in the country; being, with slight differences of detail, common to all the states, regal and republican, and extending also to the several ecclesiastical communities.

"The system I am about to describe to you," said Mr. Adamson, who was one of their principal informants on this occasion, "was established by the Müllers; the younger of whom, during the whole of his long reign, as it may be called, laboured earnestly and successfully to explain its advantages, and to perpetuate its adoption. I will put into your hands presently a little popular tract on the subject written by him, which, like the many others he wrote, is in every one's hands at this day. He sets forth in that the evils resulting, on the one hand, from retaining, or, oftener, vainly striving to retain, all laws, usages, and institutions unaltered, some of which, even though the result originally of consummate wisdom, may become utterly unsuitable to other times and altered circumstances; and, on the other hand, from frequent, sudden, and violent changes, which are apt to agitate and unsettle men's minds, and to lead to consequences not designed or foreseen,—like the pulling out of one stone from a wall, which is apt to loosen some of the others. His discussion of this subject bears much resemblance to those I lately saw in the little book you lent me the other day, by Lord Bacon,[2] who strikes me as a very able writer, and likely to be well worthy of the reputation you tell me he enjoys.

2. A little pocket edition of Bacon's Essays, one of four or five small volumes which the travellers had brought with them to beguile any occasional tedious half-hour at their halting-places, or in their boat.

"Müller goes on to say that unwise legislators have been in all ages apt to bring on themselves, not one only, but both of these classes of evils. Unmindful of the proverb, that "a stitch in time saves nine," they often, through dread of change, maintain unaltered things which manifestly want altering, at the expense of much loss and inconvenience; and when the change does come, from the inconvenience having grown to an intolerable height, it is apt to be, in consequence, a violent, hasty, and sometimes ruinous change. 'That dirt made this dust,' is a homely old saying, which he used frequently to apply in speaking of such instances, in allusion to those who in wet weather neglect to scrape off the mud from the roads; and consequently, besides being for a long time continually splashed and bemired, at length, when the mud is all dried up by the sun, they are half smothered by the dust it produces. He would always, therefore, he said, be, by choice, an *improver*, rather than a *reformer*; introducing corrections and additions, from time to time, as occasion offered, rather than letting a building become so inconvenient or ruinous as to require being pulled down and rebuilt.

"A great reformation he considered as, in all cases, a great evil; though frequently by far the least evil that circumstances admit of, and though he had himself, accordingly, been always a strenuous supporter of the great reformation of religion, notwithstanding the many evils resulting, according to him, from its having been so long delayed and so obstinately resisted. To avoid both of the opposite evils,—the liability to sudden and violent changes, and the adherence to established usage when inconvenient or mischievous,—to give the requisite stability to governments and other institutions without shutting the door against improvement,—this is a problem which both ancient and modern legislators, he thought, had not well succeeded in solving. And the same, it appears, may be said of those who have appeared in Europe since his time. Some, like the ancient Medes and Persians, and like Lycurgus, have attempted to prohibit all change; but those who constantly appeal to the wisdom of their ancestors, as a sufficient reason for perpetuating everything these have established, forget two things; first, that they cannot hope for ever to persuade all successive generations of men that there was once one generation of such infallible wisdom as to be entitled to dictate to all their descendants for ever,—so as to make the earth, in fact, the possession, not of the living, but of the dead; and, secondly, that, even supposing our ancestors gifted with such infallibility, many cases must arise in which it may be reasonably doubted whether they themselves would not have advocated, if living, changes called for by altered circumstances; even as our own forefathers, who denoted the *southern* quarter from *meridies* (noon), would not have been so foolish as to retain that language had they come to live in this hemisphere, where the sun at noon is in the north.

"The expedient of having two or more deliberative assemblies, or other authorities, in a state, whose concurrent sanction shall be requisite for enacting or abrogating laws, has often been resorted to, as a safeguard against sudden and violent measures adopted under an ebullition of feeling, yet without precluding well-weighed and deliberate changes. This expedient he thought a very good one, as far as it goes; it is adopted in various forms in each of our states. But it appeared to him that experience had proved this provision to be not alone sufficient for accomplishing fully the object he had in view, which was to give the requisite stability to those more fundamental laws which may be considered as part of the constitution of any state, (yet not so as to attempt prohibiting a wary and deliberate alteration of them,) and at the same time to afford proper facilities for introducing changes into matters of detail.

"'Nature,' said he, 'does not give the same degree of strength to the footstalks of the leaves of a tree,—destined, as these are, to be shed every year,—and to the roots, which are designed to hold the trunk fast in the ground. If she did, either the one would be far too strong or the other far too weak, or both of these inconveniences might take place at once; yet this is the error committed by almost all governments. The same machinery is provided to facilitate or to impede *every* change alike, in great or in small matters; the same mode is prescribed for the maintaining, or abrogating, or introducing of *every* law and *every* institution alike. Among you, for instance, an act for regulating the manufacture of soap, or an act which should introduce a complete change into your constitution,—which should take away or restore the liberties of half the nation,—must go through exactly the same forms, and be passed or rejected by the same authorities under the same regulations: in short, you are like a tree whose leaf-stalks and main roots have neither more nor less toughness and stoutness the one than the other.'

"Now this is a state of things which he considered as always inexpedient, and often dangerous, and which he accordingly proposed to remedy. The system which he recommended, and which has been universally adopted, is this. All our laws are divided into two classes; the ordinary or repealable laws, and the fundamental. The former are enacted, altered, or repealed much in the same manner as all laws of all other nations: but a fundamental law is one which there exists no immediate power to enact, annul, or amend; and it is forbidden by the rules of the house to propose any measure that, even incidentally, goes to defeat or interfere with the operation of any fundamental law. But it is allowed to propose, and to pass, a bill for removing any fundamental law from the list, and reducing it to an ordinary law; after which, it is open to be dealt with like any other law. So, also, it is allowed to pass a bill for placing any already existing ordinary law on the list of fundamentals.

"The enactment, therefore, or repeal of a fundamental law, may be accomplished at *two* steps, though not at one; but it is further provided that these two steps shall not take place in one session of parliament." [He was describing the details, he said, in the terms, and according to the usages, of the kingdom of Nether-London; having premised that there is a substantial agreement in principle throughout all the states on this subject.] "When it is proposed to remove a law from the list of fundamentals, the motion made is, 'that such and such a law shall, *at the close of the present session*, cease to be fundamental.' It remains, therefore, even should the motion be carried, and the act receive the royal assent, irrevocable during the existing session. When, again, the reverse measure is to be proposed, of enrolling on the list of fundamentals some existing law, an act must have first passed, authorizing the legislature to take into consideration, in the *ensuing* (or some subsequent session) the question of enrolling such and such a law.

"Lastly, another and more important safeguard against precipitancy, is that, in the case of a motion for removing any law from the list of the fundamentals, or adding one to that list, every member who does not vote *for* the motion is, by a rule of the house, reckoned, whether present or absent, as having voted *against* it. In other words, such a motion can be carried only by an *absolute* majority of the whole house, not by a mere comparative majority of members *present*."

Mr. Sibthorpe having interposed a remark, that there is something in the British constitution of the nature of a fundamental law, inasmuch as it is treason to propose the abolition of kingly government,—so that the maintenance of that government is irrevocable till a bill shall first have been passed for altering the laws of treason,—Mr. Adamson admitted that this was so far on the same footing with the law he had been describing; "but," added he, "if any one should—which I allow is highly improbable—propose such an alteration of the laws of treason, that question might legally be put to the vote in as thin a house as is competent to transact ordinary business. I think you would do well, after introducing our last regulation as to an absolute majority, to place some more of your laws on the same footing. Not that there would be any occasion for saying anything about treason. With you, as with us, it would no doubt be quite sufficient that a member should be at once 'called to order' if he presumed to make any motion contrary to the rules of the house.

"You would find, I think," he continued, "that the adoption of our system in regard to fundamental laws would tend to promote among you that comparative calmness and moderation which you have remarked in our proceedings, and to mitigate the vehemence with which, by your accounts, one set of men oppose every change, good or bad, while another seem to be hostile to everything that is established. Those who are by temper and habit most disposed to the dread of innovation, lest rash schemes should be adopted, would have their apprehensions somewhat calmed by seeing a provision made at least against any great change being introduced with inconsiderate *haste*; and those, again, who are most disposed to dread the perpetuation of abuses, might be moderated in their impatient eagerness for reform, by seeing a regular path open for the examination and remedy of anything, however consecrated by long usage, that should appear, on mature deliberation, to be evil.

"That you would be exempt from the possibility of error, or that we are so, it would be an absurd presumption to pretend. Our system does not profess to make human judgment infallible; it professes only to provide that our deliberative assemblies shall decide according to the *best* of their judgment, and shall neither retain nor reject anything, without a full opportunity at least being given for the exercise of deliberate reflection and mature discussion. To attempt more than this is mere folly. One generation of fallible men has neither the right nor the power to supersede for ever, by irrevocable laws, the judgment of all future generations of their posterity; though the endeavour to do so may delay a beneficial change, and convert it, when it does come, into a noxious one. The will of a whole nation can no more be permanently and effectually stopped in its course than the current of a river. If you dam up the regular channel, you cause it first to flood the neighbouring country, and then to work itself new and circuitous channels. You may think yourself well off if this is the worst. Should your dam be ultimately burst, a fierce and destructive deluge of revolutionary violence will succeed."

The debate which the visitors witnessed, and which led to the foregoing explanations, terminated in the removal of the law in question from the list of fundamentals. But as the minority had been considerable, the general expectation was, that before the next session,—in which alone the final repeal of the law could be proposed,—a dissolution of parliament would take place, in order that the sentiments of the people on the subject might be fully ascertained.

# CHAPTER VIII

*Mode of Election of Senators—of Representatives.—Personal Votes and Property-Votes.—Voting by Ballot.—Eligibility of Candidates.—Aboriginal Blood.—Mixed Blood.—Government Rent.—Public Expenditure.—Unwise Economy.—Choice of Statesmen.—Explanations.*

Mr. Adamson,—properly designated as the worshipful Christopher Adamson,—being himself a member of the senate of his own state of Bath, obtained for the strangers, as a special favour, permission to witness the mode of election of a senator to fill up a vacancy which had just occurred.

He explained to them, that, in this particular state, the members of the senate, or upper house, are elected by the lower house (or commons); and that the appointment is for life, or till resignation. But though in these particulars the constitution of this state differs from that of several of the others, the *mode* of election is similar to that by which several of the public functionaries are chosen in all the states. No personal canvassing, he informed them, is allowed in any case; nor is it regular to ask or to promise a vote. But at the time of the election, the president or chairman of the assembly solemnly admonishes the voters of their obligation to divest themselves, as far as possible, of all personal bias, and nominate such persons as they shall in their consciences believe to be most fit. Admonitions of this kind stand in the place of the oaths which in Europe are usually administered on such occasions. The commons-assembly having been duly convened, each member was directed to write down on separate slips of paper, and deliver to the president, the names of five persons as candidates; or, not *more* than five: for he was at liberty to write fewer; or, if he pleased, none at all.

The president next proceeded to inspect their names, and select the five that had the greatest number of votes. It so happened on this occasion that there were *six* names, of which two had each the same number of votes. This, as Mr. Adamson explained, creates no difficulty, and only prolongs in a trifling degree the business of the election. All six names were put in nomination; and each member was next called on to give his vote *against* one of the six, by giving in a paper inscribed with the name of the candidate he wished to have struck off the list. The one who had the greatest number of these counter-votes being then removed from the list, the remaining five were proposed in like manner, to have one name struck off; and the same process was repeated till only one remained, who was thereupon declared duly elected. For example: suppose the five names that, in the first instance, have most votes, to be A, B, C, D, and E, and these being put in nomination, in the counter-voting A has the most votes against him; then B, C, D, and E are proposed in like manner, and B is struck off by a majority of counter-votes; there remain C, D, and E, from which, by the same process, C and D are successively struck off: then E is the one elected.

If in any case the number of counter-votes against two of the names are equal, and that number exceeds the votes against any other one, then *both* names are struck off, except it should happen that they are the *last* two; in which case, of course, the question is, whether D or E shall be elected: and if on this question the numbers are equal, the president has the casting vote.

Mr. Adamson was about to answer the inquiries of the visitors as to the peculiar advantages proposed by this mode of election, when a blunt, humorous-looking commoner, who sat near them, interposed, by telling them that, in plain terms, this was the advantage; that each voter placed his *own friend* first, and the *best candidate* second, and so the best was elected in the end. Mr. Adamson replied with a smile, that, making due allowance for satire, there was a good deal of truth in the statement.

"It is a truth," said he, "that has been presented to you, dressed with vinegar alone, which you may easily suppose might fairly be tempered with a due proportion of oil. But I will leave that to your own reflections; only reminding you of the well-known instance of the Grecian states discussing the respective merits of the several commanders after the overthrow of Xerxes. Each state, it was observed, placed *their own* commander first on the list of merit, and allotted the second place to Themistocles the Athenian; whence it was reasonably inferred that Themistocles was clearly the most distinguished of all. Now, suppose he had been candidate for a prize in some assembly in which the Athenians were not present; he would not, you observe, have obtained a single vote according to the direct mode of voting, while on our plan he would have gained a decisive triumph. I have heard also of a new-comer in some town consulting each of his neighbours as to the choice of a physician, and fixing on the one whom most of them accounted the second-best; each placing his own family physician first."

The travellers having inquired into the mode of appointment of the lower house, were informed that the members are the representatives each of a certain town or district, as in England, America, &c.; and that they are elected for seven years at the utmost; one-seventh of the house, by lot, going out every year, but being capable, however, of re-election.

There is, besides this, a power lodged in a certain council of state and president,—for this state is a republic,—to dissolve the house and appoint a general election. In all the states there is a house of representatives, constituted substantially on the same principle. In their designations, and in some points of detail, there are several differences.

In the election of members all citizens have, in most of the states, a vote, though not all *equal* votes. Any citizen, who is unconvicted of any crime, of sound mind, and of a certain specified age, (in the state of Bath it is thirty-five,) is entitled to be enrolled as a voter, on producing a certificate of his having gone through a certain course of elementary school-learning, and attained the required proficiency. He is then entitled to what is called a *personal vote; i. e.* a vote without any reference to the amount of his property. In Bath, and some of the other states, an individual may have conferred on him the honour and privilege of a double or treble personal vote, in consideration of peculiar public services or personal qualifications.

Besides this, each individual who may pay a certain *proportion* of taxes,—*i. e.* who may possess a certain amount of taxable property,—is entitled, on that ground, to a *property-vote;*[3] if he has a certain greater amount specified,—which is more, however, than double the first,—he has a second property-vote; and so on, up to a certain limited number. In the republic of Bath, six is the utmost number of property-votes that one person can hold; but this varies in the several states; the distinction of personal and property-votes, and the power of holding more than one of the latter, are regulations common to all.

3. Any property not taxable,—as, for instance, professional income,—the holder may, if he think fit, enroll as equivalent to so much land, and pay taxes accordingly, which entitles him to a corresponding number of votes.

"This part of our system," Mr. Adamson remarked to them, "is not so much unlike that of Great Britain as you had at the first glance conceived: for with you, if a man chance to have landed property in several *different counties,* he is entitled to a vote in each; and this is nearly equivalent to his having several votes in one county, should all the property chance to be in that one. The anomaly is with *you;* in giving one man more direct influence in the election of the legislature than another, who, perhaps, has double his estate, but all within one county. I say," continued he, "*direct* influence; because, indirectly, a rich man among you does, it appears, influence his tenants, tradesmen, and other dependents in their votes. With us, the weight which property has, and ought to have, is allowed to operate *directly* and *openly*: with you, on the system of single votes, it does not.

"And accordingly you apprehend, I find, a danger in the threatened introduction of the ballot; as tending to place the richest and poorest on a footing of democratical equality, by taking away the indirect influence of the one over the votes of the other. And it is remarkable that the tendency of the ballot to produce this effect,—which is manifestly the great *danger* to be apprehended from it,—seems to be *asserted* by its advocates among you, and *denied* by its opponents. With us, on the contrary, there is no such consequence to be apprehended; and, accordingly, our voting for representatives is always by ballot. On our system, this is not only unobjectionable but highly important; for, as the successful candidate is elected by the majority of *votes*, while it is possible that his opponent might be supported by a much greater number of *voters*, it would be very inexpedient to let this be publicly displayed and recorded; as it might tend to array the wealthier and poorer classes against each other.

"On the whole," added he, "our system seems to be the simplest and most effectual for preserving that principle which *must* be maintained in every *good* representative system; viz. that *persons* and *property* should both be represented. The democrat aims at a representation of *persons alone*; at putting on a political level those who have the largest stake in the country, and those who have little or none. The aristocrat (or rather, oligarchist) is for representing *property alone*; as if the *taxes* imposed by the legislature towards the expenses of the state were everything, and the *life and liberty* of individuals, which may be affected by the laws passed, were nothing. The true wisdom, surely, is to take *both* into account, and to provide that both persons and property shall be duly represented."

In all the states but one, all persons are eligible to a seat in the lower house,—that of representatives,—who possess certain property and personal qualifications. In that one,—the kingdom of Upper-London, a small state, which was separated, above a hundred years since, from that of Nether-London,—a sort of hereditary restriction exists, which, at the first glance, appeared to the travellers exceedingly whimsical. No one is eligible to their commons' assembly who is not descended, or married to one who is, from both blacks and whites.

The origin of the regulation was this:—Before the state was separated, the district which constitutes its present territory was occupied by a considerable proportion of blacks, viz. the descendants of the allied and reclaimed aboriginals formerly described. It was observed by the then king of Nether-London, (then called New-London,) that the whites of pure blood were beginning to hold aloof, not only from the blacks, but from those of mixed breed, and to disdain associating with them on equal terms, however personally deserving. To remedy this state of things, and prevent a mutual alienation between two sets of fellow-citizens, the king,—who seems to have inherited something of the eccentric, original, and daring character of the younger Müller, from a daughter of whom he was descended,—devised the plan, which, with the concurrence of the legislature, he carried into effect, for constituting this district—a thriving and, in other respects, promising one—into a distinct state, under some peculiar regulations.

A brother of his own was appointed the first king of it,—whose wife is said to have been a lady of beauty and accomplishments, though she had a slight mixture of aboriginal blood. Inducements were held out to several of the most respectable and intelligent persons in various states who were of mixed race, to come and settle in the new kingdom. Some of the ablest of these,—who, by the bye, are said to have had a considerable over-proportion of European blood in their veins,—together with others of purely white race, were nominated as the original senate (or upper house); and the lower house was, by a fundamental law, to consist exclusively, and for ever, of persons of mixed race, or who are married to such. And, to this day, no one is eligible who cannot prove his descent, or his wife's, from blacks and whites.

This, however, is easily done at present; for the descent may be ever so remote, the mixture ever so unequal. Every one, therefore, is eligible, of whom any ancestor has been enrolled as such. There are, accordingly, many members of the house who, perhaps, have not above $1/16$ or $1/32$ of aboriginal blood; and, indeed, most of the population are at present not very dissimilar from Europeans in feature and complexion, and yet are qualified, as far as the above rule is concerned, for a seat in the house.

The plan was at first laughed at, as whimsical, by many of the Southlanders themselves; but the expediency of it in promoting mutual respect and speedy amalgamation between the two races, who were thus *both alike excluded* from an important branch of the legislature, was so apparent, and the joke was so good-humouredly joined in by those who were the objects of it, that the laughter was soon divested of all bitterness. The satirists had suggested, as a symbol for the new state, two swans,—an Australian black swan (Cygnus ater) and white European,—lovingly entwining their necks: on which the Upper-Londoners immediately adopted this as the arms of the kingdom; and so it remains to this day, with the motto of "Nimium ne crede colori." The state, though one of the smaller ones, (its population about two hundred and fifty thousand,) is prosperous, and its citizens respectable, intelligent, and polite.

In most of the states, there are few or no considerable taxes, except a land tax; and in many of them even this is not heavy, from the government being in possession of considerable tracts of land, which in some instances have become very valuable from having been covered with buildings, wharfs, &c. [The word "tax" is used as best conveying to English ears the sense intended. They themselves call it "government-*rent*;" for they consider the state as alone holding what we call the fee-simple of all land, which it assigns to individuals, either for terms of years at a stipulated rent, or in perpetuity, subject to what we should call a land-tax.]

On the whole, Mr. Sibthorpe is of opinion, that, taking into consideration the very small military (and, of course, no naval) establishments, and also the comparative wealth of these and the European states, the government revenues are proportionably greater in the Southland states than in those of Europe,—the revenue that is actually *expended in the public service* each year; for he does not take into account, as a part of our revenue, the enormous sum annually paid as interest on the national debt. These states having happily been exempt from the prodigal expenditure of wars, have no national debt. Their public expenditure is, however, what we should be apt to call profuse in the payment of public functionaries. All are paid, even the representatives; and to most offices is attached, besides what may be considered an ample salary in reference to the prevailing style of living, a comfortable retiring pension: sinecures however, strictly so called,—*i. e.* payments for *no* services, either present or *past*,—are not known. When the more frugal system, in reference to this point, that prevails among us, was described to them, and also the prevailing clamour for still further reductions on that head, they gave it as their opinion that there could not be money worse saved, and that is must be a great wonder if we were well governed.

"The natural tendency," they urged, "of a system of *frugal* government in this sense, is, to obtain a worse commodity. Try the experiment," they said, "of being frugal to your physicians, and reduce their fees to half-crowns, and you will have a half-crown's worth of skill instead of a guinea's worth. You will still have plenty of physicians, but we should not like to be under their hands. While a man of talents and character, with a liberal education and industry, can realize a handsome and secure income in some of your learned professions, you cannot expect him, especially if he have a family to provide for, and but little private fortune, to give up a lucrative employment, and devote himself to the labours of political life, either gratuitously, or with an uncertain recompense in view. He will either keep aloof from public business, or will bestow on it a hurried, divided, and secondary attention. Thus, political business, and ultimately political power, is thrown into the hands of one or both of two classes of men:—those of *large estates*; and *adventurers*,—men, who, for want of character, or of steady application, are not succeeding in any reputable and lucrative profession, and therefore see nothing better to do than to take their chance in the profession—an ill-paid and precarious one, as it seems to be among you—of politics.

"Many persons of both these classes, among you, may, we doubt not, be possessed of high qualifications; but it seems evident that with so large a total number as you possess of educated and intelligent gentry, you practically limit your choice to a very small proportion of them for persons to conduct public affairs; and these affairs, therefore, we should expect to find conducted, if not ill, yet by no means so well as they might be. We should expect to find the department of government—one of such paramount importance—not so well filled as many subordinate departments; and that there would be among you a larger proportionate number of highly qualified legal, military, and naval men, for instance, of engineers, artisans, &c. than of statesmen.

"You are to observe," they added, "that we are only throwing out our *conjectures*: we are ready and willing to stand corrected. You must know how the matter of fact stands; which may perhaps be at variance with our anticipations, through the operation of some causes we are not aware of. But we lay before you our notions and expectations, as the thought strikes ourselves."

[There follows here, in the memoranda of the travellers, the explanations they gave, in answer to the foregoing remarks, of our institutions and usages,—the reasons by which they are vindicated,—and the practical working of them. But all this, though of course most interesting to the persons to whom it was addressed, would probably not be so to our readers, who must of course be familiar with discussions relative to our own institutions and customs, and curious rather to learn particulars concerning those of a strange nation, however unreasonable and whimsical their novelty may cause them to appear. For this reason, we have, in several other places as well as here, omitted much that we find recorded of the descriptions and discussions laid before the Southlanders by their guests; inserting only what was necessary to make their descriptions intelligible.]

# CHAPTER IX

*Prediction Office.—Prophecies.—Useful Register.—Political Bustlers.—Disposal of Land.—Rents.—Laws of Tenantry.—Government Loans.*

Among the other political curiosities, as they may be called, which came to the knowledge of the travellers, was a most whimsical institution, existing in several of the states, called a "prediction office;" viz. an establishment consisting of two or three inspectors and a few clerks, appointed to receive from any one, on payment of a trifling fee, any sealed-up *prediction*, to be opened at a time specified by the party himself. His name is to be signed to the prediction *within*; and on the outer cover is inscribed the date of its delivery, and the time when the seal is to be broken. There is no pretence made to supernatural prophetic powers; only, to supposed political sagacity.

At stated times, the inspectors break the seal of those papers whose term is elapsed, and examine the contents. In a great majority of cases, as might be expected, these predictions turn out either false, nugatory, or undecided: false, if contradicted by events; nugatory, if containing nothing but what had been naturally and generally anticipated by all,—like our almanacks, which foretell showers in April, heat in summer, and cold in winter; or undecided, when proceeding hypothetically on some *condition* which does not take place,—as when a man foretells that *if* such a measure be adopted, so and so will ensue; if then the measure is *not* adopted, the prediction remains undecided. But here and there a case occurs in which a man has foretold truly something not generally expected, and the foreseeing of which evinces, accordingly, more or less of sagacity. In such a case he is summoned to receive an honourable certificate to that effect. And the travellers were assured that some of their most eminent men, who afterwards attained to offices of dignity and trust, had been first called into notice from obscurity by means of this office. The other predictions are kept and registered, but not made public, except when the author of any of them is named as a candidate for any public office.

Previously to any such appointment, the inspectors are bound to look over their register, and produce, as a set-off against a candidate's claims, any unsuccessful prediction he may have sent in. "Oh that he were here," exclaims Mr. Sibthorpe, "'to write me down an ass!' Many a man there is to whom we have committed important public trusts, who, if such an institution had existed among us, would be found to have formally recorded, under the influence of self-conceit, his own incapacity." He seems to consider this portion of the effects of the plan as hardly less useful than the other,—the establishment of the claims of some to superior foresight.

"There is," he adds, "among our political bustlers usually a great squabble when any event takes place on the question, whether any one, and who, may claim the honour of having foreseen it; and ill-founded claims are often admitted. Moreover, a prediction publicly uttered will often have had, or be supposed to have had, a great share in bringing about its own fulfilment. He who gives out, for instance, that the people will certainly be dissatisfied with such and such a law, is, in this, doing his utmost to *make* them dissatisfied. And this being the case in all unfavourable, as well as favourable, predictions, some men lose their deserved credit for political sagacity through their fear of contributing to produce the evils they apprehend; while others, again, do contribute to evil results by their incapacity to keep their anticipations locked up in their own bosoms, and by their dread of not obtaining deserved credit. For such men, this office," says he, "provides a relief like that which the servant of King Midas found by telling his secret to the hole he dug in the ground; only there are here no whispering reeds to divulge it."

The mode in which the states that have considerable tracts of uncleared land in their territory usually dispose of these from time to time, struck the travellers as judicious and simple. When, from increasing population, a demand arises for a fresh portion of land requiring to be cleared and brought into cultivation, each person who desires to become a settler rents from the state (which, as has been before observed, is always held to be the sole proprietor in fee-simple of its whole territory,) a suitable allotment, at a rent which is always very small, and often merely nominal. He obtains a lease of this for a term of years,—commonly twenty-one,—either at this nominal rent for the whole term, or with a trifling increase for the last seven or fourteen years of it. At the end of the term, it is *divided* between him and the state; part being made over to him in perpetuity, (subject to the general land-tax, or government-rent, as it is called,) and the other part reverting to the state. The proportions vary according as the expenses of reclaiming the land are greater or less. If the requisite outlay is considerable, the settler retains, perhaps, two-thirds, or even three-fourths, of the allotment; if the reverse, his share will be half, or one-third. In all cases, the proportions in which it is to be divided are a matter of express agreement previously to his first entering on the farm. Then, in order to secure a fair division of the land in respect of *quality*,—that the more fertile and the poorer land, the more and the less improved, may be duly apportioned,—recourse is had to the obvious plan of "one to divide and the other to choose."

Suppose, for instance, the tenant is to be entitled by his contract to one-half; then, at the end of his term, he divides his holding into any two portions, at his pleasure, and gives notice to the state-surveyors, who, after due inspection, assign one of them (whichever they please) to him. Besides this, however, it is very often made a separate point of special agreement in the first instance, that, at the end of his term, he shall have the option of obtaining, at an advantageous rate, a lease for a further term of the portion assigned to the state. He is to be allowed to hold it at a rent below the market price. No *definite sum*, however, is fixed, and the land is offered to the highest bidder; but the tenant who shall have made such a contract as has been just alluded to, is to have a certain *portion of his rent remitted*,—suppose 20, 30, or 40 per cent. according to the agreement. He is thus enabled,—supposing all parties to agree in their calculations of the land,—to outbid the rest. Suppose A. to be the former tenant, and that the bidders for the land do not offer quite so much as one hundred pounds rent for it, and that he is under agreement to have twenty per cent. remitted; if he then thinks the land worth eighty pounds, he may bid one hundred pounds, and will be the successful competitor. But should A. not think it worth while to pay so much as eighty pounds, while B. is willing to pay one hundred pounds, then B. obtains it. Any bidder, to whom the land is knocked down, forfeits a certain deposit in the event of his not completing the bargain.

This mode of procedure it was found necessary to introduce on account of the great and unexpected alterations in the value of land, which, in a new settlement especially, may take place by means of new towns, roads, and other improvements. A certain *proportion* of the market price, therefore, was fixed on, instead of a certain *definite sum*, as a more equitable mode of adjusting the amount of the advantage agreed for.

All rents, whether for lands or houses, and whether from a tenant of the state or of an individual, are payable a year *in advance*; in other words, are payable, not for the year that is *past*, but for the year that is to come.

[The rent, in short, is like the purchase-money of an estate, which is to be paid *before* the title-deeds are delivered and the possession transferred.]

In like manner, with them, rent is the *purchase-money* of the house or land *for one year*; and the tenant has no claim upon it till that is paid. Rent, accordingly, is not recoverable or claimable as a *debt*; nor is there any such thing as distraining. It is, in fact, no debt; but at the end of the year, if the rent, or rather purchase-money, for the *ensuing* year have not been paid, the occupier ceases to have any interest in the land, and is exactly in the situation of a tenant whose lease has expired. If, however, he has *agreed* to take the house or land at a certain annual rent for a term of years, and fails to fulfil the engagement, he may be sued for a breach of contract, and, as in the case of any other breach of contract, will have to pay damages according to the circumstance of the case.

The travellers suggested, on this being first described, that it must be an inconvenience to a farmer to pay a sum of money out of his capital before he has got anything from his land. But they learned that, to prevent this, it is customary to let a farm for a term of years, and to fix the rent for the *first* year (to a new tenant) at a mere nominal sum. "At the end of each year, therefore," said they, "we have our rents coming in, just as you have in England; and if (as you say is common in England) the same tenant and his family continue to renew from time to time, the landlord is just in the same situation in both countries.

"It is only when there is occasion to get rid of a bad tenant, and put in a new one, that there need be any difference; and when that is the case, your landlord is not, by your account, always better off than ours; but, on the contrary, sometimes loses *more* than *one* year's rent, and incurs a great deal of trouble and law-expense besides."

New settlers, becoming government-tenants under the arrangement above described, are sometimes in want of sufficient capital for the requisite improvements, especially irrigation, which is conducted on a great scale. In such cases, the state often advances a loan at moderate interest, secured on the land that is to be the tenant's portion at the end of his term.

There are no usury laws in the country; every one lets either his land, his money, or any other property, on whatever terms the parties agree on.

# CHAPTER X

*An Arrest.—Criminal Jurisprudence.—Jurymen.—Qualification of Jurors.—Syndics.—Royal Privilege.—Proceedings in Court.—Witnesses.—The Verdict.—Unanimity in Juries.—Decision of the Judge.—Prevarication.—Oaths.—False Witnesses.—Inconsistency in requiring Oaths.—Public Opinion.—Marriage.—Succession to the Crown.*

While the travellers were in conversation with their new friends, a crowd was observed passing through the streets, as if some circumstance of interest had just occurred. On inquiry, it turned out, that one of the people had been arrested on rather an important charge, and that the proper officers were leading him off in custody. The travellers were very much struck by the demeanour of the people, which seemed to indicate respect for the authorities, and, at the same time, a delicacy of feeling towards the individual who was arrested, though not yet proved guilty. They became naturally curious to obtain information concerning their criminal jurisprudence, their mode of trial and of punishment.

Mr. Adamson observed, that though any of the company present would be competent to detail to him the particulars of their practice, because it was held a general duty for every respectable person to have a knowledge of this kind; yet that as one of their judges, Sir Peter, was present in the room, it would be, perhaps, more satisfactory that they should seek the information from him. Accordingly, on being introduced to him, they started the subject by saying they were anxious to know whether the Southlanders had retained the trial by jury, as it was practised in England. He replied, that the first settlers had retained the usage in this respect with which they had been familiar; but that, as the settlement advanced, they found it expedient to adopt some modifications of it, which they regarded as very important. These modifications related, he said, chiefly to the selection of jurors, or, as they were termed in the settlement, syndics, and also to the degree in which unanimity was requisite for a verdict. "Our judges," he said, "found speedily that all men, even in the same rank of life, were not equally to be entrusted with this important function; and also, that requiring perfect unanimity was frequently the cause, either that no verdict was arrived at, or a wrong one,—sometimes, even against the opinion of the majority.

"These inconveniences," he said, "did not develope themselves for a considerable period. On our first settlement, when the minds of the people were chiefly occupied in providing for their daily wants, we found that the intelligence of each man might be very safely measured by the successfulness of his industry; and we allowed our jurymen to be selected indiscriminately from amongst those who were able to support themselves creditably by their own exertions. But we found, subsequently, that successful industry was not always accompanied by that intelligence and sagacity which would enable men to decide on the merits of conflicting evidence.

"We have instituted, therefore, an examination for the purpose of ascertaining fitness. As each man becomes of age, he may, if he thinks himself prepared, submit himself to the assembled judges, who question him with regard to the laws of evidence; and, if they are satisfied both as to his intelligence and moral character, he is marked as a person capable of discharging this function."

The English travellers replied with a smile, that few in England would be found, probably, to submit themselves to such an examination; that, though they prided themselves as a nation upon the possession of the right to trial by jury, yet that each man considered the office as a burthen, which he was anxious to roll over upon his neighbour, as interfering with the employment of his time; and that this feeling would certainly be strengthened if an examination were required.

"We," said Mr. Benson, "have established an order of syndics; and it is considered honourable to be enrolled amongst the number. We have conferred certain privileges on the order; for instance, while we give to every man who has not been disqualified by crime a right to one vote in the selection of parliamentary representatives, we give three votes to each syndic; and this in addition to the increased number of votes which he may have arising from the manner in which we have graduated property. This latter circumstance has, however, nothing to do with the matter in question. What I wish you to remark now is, that we regard any man of sufficient intelligence to be a syndic, as entitled on that account to exercise a greater influence than others in the selection of those who are to frame our laws."

On being asked whether the examination was really strict, Sir Peter answered that the strictness of course varied with the dispositions and sense of duty possessed by the existing judges; but that rejection was a very common occurrence. If this proceeded from moral objection, it was exceedingly difficult for the person to gain admission afterwards; this could only be effected by very conspicuous and continued good conduct. If, however, the rejection arose from a want merely of adequate knowledge, the individual was always at liberty to submit himself freely for re-examination, when in his own judgment he had acquired it. It was not considered creditable for any syndic to give his daughter in marriage to any one who was not enrolled with himself in the rank of the intelligent. Thus, he said, public opinion has conspired with civil privileges to render it important to each man to acquire this rank.

On being asked whether the number of syndics was considerable, he replied that it was, and that it was found by the periodical census that it was bearing an increasing proportion to the number of citizens generally; that they regarded this, in fact, as one of the tests of increasing civilization,—more especially because their experience proved that the examination became more strict and enlarged, according as the general intelligence of the country was increased. Persons would be rejected now, who, some years back, would have been, on the same acquirements, sure of admission.

"I am describing to you, however," he said, "the regulations which prevail in this particular state. In the other states in union with us, many variations may be observed, though all agree in selecting syndics by examination. The number of votes, for instance, given to a syndic, as such, is different in different states. Again, in some states, the number of syndics is not left indefinite, as with us, but is limited."

Sir Peter went on to observe, that the names of all the syndics were regularly arranged on rolls, each of which, in this particular state, contained not less than one hundred and twenty names. These rolls, a day or two before the commencement of the assizes, were presented to the judge, who drew from them a certain number by lot. The persons so drawn were then summoned to attend the court; and when any cause was entered upon for trial, the plaintiff and defendant were each allowed to assign some rule according to which triers should be taken from the roll of attendants summoned for that day,—as, for instance, every third or fifth or tenth individual, commencing from the top or bottom of the list, till the number of twelve was completed. "Thus," he said, "having taken precaution that none but men of intelligence should have their names enrolled, we must be careful that all packing of juries shall be out of the question. Neither of the interested parties can influence, either directly or indirectly, the selection of those who have to try the case."

In those states which have a regal (or *quasi*-regal) form of government, the sovereign has, as with us, the privilege of pardoning criminals, but with one exception; attempts on the life of the sovereign himself cannot receive the royal pardon, except through the means of an address to the throne from the whole legislative body.

"It is," say they, "very indelicate at least, to let the king be placed in so invidious a situation as that of having to decide on the fate of one who assailed his life."

"And now," said Sir Peter, "having given you such preliminary information as you could not obtain by merely attending our courts, I would propose to you to defer any further enquiries respecting our modes of trial. These you can best judge of by actually witnessing them for yourselves. Come with me to-morrow: I will take care that you shall have a convenient seat. Observe narrowly for yourselves, and, when the business of the day is over, put any questions you please to me on any point in which you perceive our customs differ from yours, and I will explain to you our reasons for such changes."

The travellers thankfully availed themselves of this offer; and next morning, accordingly, they accompanied Sir Peter to the court. Immediately on his taking his seat, general silence was proclaimed, when the regular officer read from a paper the character of the suit to be tried, the names of the parties, and of the witnesses whom each party had summoned to give evidence. The witnesses were then called forward, and placed under the care of an officer, whom they accompanied out of court. Sir Peter whispered to the travellers, that in no case did they permit one witness to hear the testimony given by another.

The jury were then selected in the manner already pointed out by Mr. Benson on the previous evening. On their taking their seats the trial immediately proceeded; but, as the travellers were surprised to observe, without any administration of oaths. They remarked also, as each witness was called, it was stated whether he was a syndic or not. In case he was a syndic, the examination proceeded at once; but when a witness not a syndic was called upon, the judge urged on him, in a brief but solemn manner, to remember, in giving his testimony, that his thoughts and words were known to the Searcher of hearts.

As each witness concluded his evidence, the judge asked the opinion of the triers as to whether that witness had shown a wish to prevaricate. In one instance it happened that an affirmative answer was returned, when the witness was immediately given over to the custody of an attending officer.

When the evidence had been all heard, and commented on by counsel, the names of the twelve triers were written on slips of paper, and four names were drawn by lot. The four triers who answered to these names were then separated from the rest, and the judge required them to declare their decision within half an hour. They were then allowed to retire.

Before the termination of the allotted time they returned into court, and declared that they were agreed. In one, however, of the trials which subsequently took place, it happened that, at the end of the half-hour, they announced that the votes were divided. Four names of the remaining triers were then selected by lot, as before; and the judge informed them that he would expect their decision in twenty minutes.

At the expiration of the time they came forward, and pronounced a decision in favour of the defendant. They were then called upon to state whether, in their opinion, any witness had given testimony which he must have known to be false. They replied, none. The witness charged with prevarication was then called forward, and allowed to plead what he thought fit in his own defence. He failed to clear himself; and thereupon, having been very solemnly reprimanded by the judge, was declared suspended for a twelvemonth from exercising any vote for a representative, or holding any civil employment during that time.

The travellers remained in court, on this and some subsequent days, to witness other trials, and perceived that the same process was gone through, with such variations in the results as might be expected. They remarked, for instance, that one witness, who was a syndic, was declared guilty of prevarication, and that he was instantly pronounced to be degraded from this office for ever; but it did not happen during three days that the triers denounced any witness as having been guilty of deliberate falsehood.

On joining Sir Peter in the evening of the last day, the travellers observed to him that they had been very much pleased with the orderly arrangements of the court, and the quiet attention of the spectators. "We need scarcely," they observed, "make any remarks with respect to your not requiring unanimity in your juries. The inconvenience of this requisition has been fully acknowledged amongst ourselves, though our practice has been suffered to remain unchanged. We hope, indeed, that our poet goes too far in saying that 'wretches hang, that jurymen may dine!' Still, a suspicion even that this, or, more probably, the converse may be the case, is very injurious to the respect which ought to be entertained for legal decisions. And we must admit, also, we have heard of one juryman complaining that no verdict was arrived at because he was associated with eleven obstinate men who would not agree to his opinion. We strongly suspect, therefore, that you are justified in the change which you have made. We would wish to know, however, whether it does not sometimes happen that the discrepancy of opinion, which we perceived to have occurred on one occasion in the first section of your jury, may not take place also in the second, and even in the third. Amongst us, when a discrepancy of this kind takes place, the only remedy we have discovered is to throw as much punishment and ridicule as we can upon the whole jury. We lock them up for as long a time as their constitutions can endure without actual loss of life; and when our judge is leaving the county, we order that the jury shall be placed in a cart, and drawn out after the judge to the boundaries of the district. This certainly does not remedy the evil arising from want of unanimity in the particular case; but it may operate upon the minds of jurors in other cases, and induce each of them to yield somewhat of his own opinion, not always to the majority or the wisest, but to the most stubborn."

"If this yielding, however," said Sir Peter, "proceeded, not from conviction, but from fear of punishment and ridicule, it may be doubted at least whether your juries are always, in point of fact, unanimous in their verdicts. Many of your jurors may have a strong suspicion, at least, that the verdict should be in some respects different from that which is actually returned. When no verdict has been given in, the public are aware that there was a difference of opinion amongst the jury; but when they do deliver a verdict, it cannot be concluded, in every case, that there was even ultimately an unanimity. We think it better that every man should be left free, after having heard the opinions of others, and consulted with them, to declare what was his own ultimate conviction."

"But supposing," the travellers said, "that no decision is come to by the jury after the third attempt, have you made any provision to meet this difficulty?"

"In that case," said Sir Peter, "the judge decides, as we think he fairly might. Where the contest is about property, we conceive it better that a positive decision should be arrived at rather than that the matter should be left doubtful. We give then, however, a power of appeal to twelve judges, who examine the evidence, and ultimately decide. In a criminal trial we give an absolute power of decision to the judge, leaving him however at liberty if he pleases to pronounce a verdict merely of Not proved; in which case, this verdict is recorded against the supposed culprit, as affecting his character in case of any subsequent charge against him."

"We strongly suspect," said the English travellers, "that you are right in this part of your practice; but," added they with a smile, "you have taken us by surprise in one respect; we did not know you had adopted the opinion of the Quakers we were describing to you,—that oaths were forbidden by the Christian religion."

"We have adopted their practice," said Sir Peter, "but not their principles. We do not conceive oaths unlawful, but inexpedient."

The travellers said, "We perceive you have a substitute for oaths, as far as witnesses are concerned, because you make the triers pronounce as to whether any has been in their opinion guilty of prevarication, while his testimony is still fresh in their recollections: and we also observed that, when the whole trial is over, the triers are called on to decide whether any witness has been in their opinion guilty of perjury. We suppose," they observed, "that you have a punishment when an affirmative answer is returned?"

"We make the punishment," said Mr. Benson, "proportioned to the effect which would have been produced by his testimony, supposing it to have been believed true. In all cases, of course, he forfeits office and civil privileges, as a person unworthy of their exercise; and, in some cases, he is fined heavily, or his property is made to pass on to his heir, as if he himself were dead. He may be sentenced, again, to imprisonment and hard labour, or even to death, should his testimony have endangered the life of another."

"We think," said the travellers, "that this is certainly capable of securing truth fully as much, and even more than can be effected by an oath; for many will shun falsehood, through fear of detection, who would not scruple to break an oath. But," they said, "the decision of your juries would appear to us more to be relied on if that decision was given under the sanction of an oath."

"We doubt it," said Mr. Benson, "and we strongly suspect that you do not really differ from us in opinion, though you do in practice; because in the case of Quakers and others, who are exempted from the legal necessity of taking an oath, you are in the habit of relying fully as much on their testimony as if they had taken an oath. Now this does not happen, I believe, from your thinking more highly of Quakers than of others, but from your conviction that oaths do not supply any real security. To us, however, it appears that oaths proceed altogether on an erroneous principle. It looks as if you thought that God would not attend to perjury, unless his attention were specially called to the matter. And this is to think as the savages do, who conceive their gods are often asleep or on a journey, and that they notice nothing except so far as they are solicited."

"But would not your principle," said the English travellers, "equally militate against prayer of any kind; because God must know our wants, whether we supplicate him or not?"

"True," replied the other; "he knows our wants, but not our humble applications to him for aid, unless we make such application. Now it is to our prayers, not to our wants, that his gifts are promised. He does not say 'Need, and ye shall have; want, and ye shall find;' but 'Ask, and ye shall have; seek, and ye shall find.' In the case of false witness, it is otherwise. God will punish the perjurer, in another world at least, whether he calls upon him to do so or not. Of this every man should be reminded whenever he is called upon solemnly to speak truth. Your practice," he added, "of requiring an oath in each case, arose at that period when it was supposed that God would always interfere by a special judgment. You have given this up as far as trial by single combat is concerned; but you have retained what grew out of the same persuasions, though, in point of fact, you as little believe your principles in this case as in the former. Trial by jury, your great boast, is, as practised by you, a remnant of the superstitious ordeal of your barbarian ancestors. But the strangest part of all is, that, while you require oaths, you proclaim at the same time your belief that every man is ready to perjure himself if he has the smallest pecuniary interest in doing so. Thus, for instance, you do not admit the testimony, even on oath, of any man who may gain or lose a shilling in consequence of his testimony. It is not a bare suspicion that he *may* bear false witness, and a consequent *abatement* of confidence in his testimony, but a full confidence that he *will* be ready to perjure himself, and a total *exclusion* of his testimony.

"Again, you appear to us to think that oaths may *wear out*; and you therefore renew them from time to time. When a man is appointed to some situation, you compel him to take certain oaths. Should he continue to hold the same situation, all is well; but if he has so distinguished himself as to be noticed by his superiors, and promoted to a higher office,—as, for instance, when a clergyman is transferred from a curacy, or from an inferior to a better parish,—instantly he seems to fall under the suspicion of the law, and a renewal of his oaths is exacted from him.

"All this," he said, "appears to us not only unnecessary, but even calculated to weaken the general sense of public duty. To require an oath in *any* case, is to confess an expectation that men, when not under this obligation, are likely to tell falsehoods: to require an oath on being invested with office, is to state that society does not expect men to perform duties from any sense of their importance, or any obligation arising out of the trust reposed in the individuals, but from a principle of a distinct and different kind. Now, to proclaim such an opinion, has, we think, a strong tendency to make it true. We should apprehend, at least, that in all cases (and, I may add, on all points) when no oaths are required, there would be a less active and conscientious discharge of duties, because the only acknowledged and legally recognised ground of obligation does not exist; just as the oaths of witnesses tend to produce a disregard of veracity in ordinary transactions. This would be the natural result. But, we must say, from what we have observed of your characters, and from many things you have mentioned to us, that you have impressed us with the belief that much public spirit exists amongst you in spite of your system. We apprehend, in fact, that public opinion amongst you is, in many respects, in advance of your legal code. But we should like to know your own opinion. Do you conceive, in general, that those who hold such employments as are guarded by oaths perform their duties *in consequence* of the oath, or because they conceive that integrity and due attention are right for their own sakes?"

The travellers replied they were of opinion that most men acted from the latter feeling, and that the oath seldom recurred to the memory of any. "In fact," they said, "most persons amongst us would hold themselves affronted if they were told that they were trusted in any particular, not on account of their general reputation and their own sense of rectitude, but because they had taken an oath."

"We are anxious," said Sir Peter, "that law should throw no obstacles in the growth of the feelings you describe, and we therefore exact, not only no promissory oaths, but no promises to perform duties. Of course we allow, and legally enforce, contracts in all cases, when any individual consents to do something he was otherwise not bound to, in consideration of a promise made to him by another; as, for instance, when he lets him land in consequence of a stipulated rent. Promises of this kind are committed to writing, and legally enforced. Or, to take a more important case—marriage. Here the parties enter upon a new course of life, in consequence of an engagement which each makes to the other: we enforce, therefore, by law the fulfilment of that engagement."

The English travellers asked with a smile, "Do you always find *that* engagement fulfilled in its spirit? Does your contract secure in all cases mutual kindness and good temper?"

"That," said Sir Peter, "is beyond the reach of civil law. As far as the civil rights of either party, or of their children, are concerned, we enforce them by a civil contract, undertaken in the presence of civil magistrates. Here the power of the law stops. But we recommend, and public opinion sanctions our recommendation, that every church should add a religious ceremony; not for the purpose of enforcing the civil obligation, for that we make a matter of the civil law, but for the purpose of impressing the minds of both parties with a due sense of the moral obligations they undertake. The forbearance and mutual kindness essential for happiness in the marriage state are the fruits, not of civil contract, (since they are not of a nature to be enforced by coercion,) but of moral principle; and our opinion is, that this should be strengthened by whatever religious service each church may consider most impressive.

"Thus, again, we have no coronation oath. When our king dies, his heir immediately succeeds as a matter of course, and with the full knowledge that he is under an obligation to govern according to the prescribed constitution. So far our customs are like your own. Amongst you, however, after the king has actually entered upon his office, and not unfrequently in some considerable time after, you exact of him an oath. This seems to us very like constituting two different kinds of regal government, namely that of an uncrowned and of a crowned king."

The English travellers replied, that they regarded the power and duty of the king as precisely the same previously and subsequently to his coronation oath.

"We know that," said Sir Peter; "and we therefore conclude that you yourselves do not regard the oath as of the least importance."

# CHAPTER XI

*Punishment awarded to Criminals.—Capital Punishments.—Plea of Insanity.—Penitentiaries.—Houses of Correction.—Improvement in Laws.—Periodical Publications.—Editors of Newspapers.—State of Literature.*

The travellers proceeded to ask some further questions, which had been suggested to them by what they had observed in the course of the trials they had witnessed.

"We perceived," said they, "that the punishment most frequently awarded was that of confinement in a penitentiary; instead, however, of naming the period of confinement, it was generally announced that the terms of confinement would be determined subsequently. We wish to know the reason of this procedure."

"We do not," replied Sir Peter, "in most cases regulate the confinement by time, but in another way. We require that each man should perform a certain quantity of daily labour, as a compensation—though, of course, often a very inadequate one—for his maintenance; and whatever he can earn above this, is placed in a bank for him. Each man is sentenced to earn a sum, regulated according to his trade, state of health, and other circumstances. When he has earned this sum, he is set at liberty. We think this has a double advantage: it encourages him to labour, because he is made aware that his own industry will affect the period of his confinement; and this has a tendency to create in him a permanent habit of industry. Again, the sum of money he has earned being given to him when released, he is not thrown on the world as a pauper, exposed by his very destitution to fresh temptation, but has the means of carrying on some species of industry.

"We have also as a punishment *secret* branding (usually on the back), performed in the way of tattooing, as your sailors do. Every culprit is examined as to whether he had been thus branded; in which case, the punishment for any subsequent crime is always the more severe. At the same time, as the brand is secret, the individual is not exposed on that account to the scoffs of his neighbours, which might make him regardless of character and produce a hardness of disposition. These are our most ordinary punishments.

"In case of murder, however, and some few other crimes, we resort to capital punishments. This is restricted, as I have intimated, to very few species of delinquency; but when those are perpetrated, the punishment of death is rigidly enforced and speedily inflicted. In any punishment prompt execution adds greatly to the terror; but in this more particularly, because death, *some time or other,* is a sentence passed by nature upon all men."

[Here occurs, as a marginal note to Mr. Sibthorpe's memoranda, a quotation from Shakspeare's dialogue of Pistol and Fluellin:—

*Pistol.*—Base caitiff! *thou shalt die.*

*Fluellin.*—You say fery true, scald knave, *when Cot's coot pleasure is.*]

The infliction of all punishments, including capital, is private; that is, is in the presence only of certain official persons, appointed to witness and certify the due execution of the sentence. The travellers could not but acknowledge the brutalising and noxiously hardening effects of our public executions.

"To show you the strictness," observed Sir Peter, "with which our penal code is administered, I must mention to you that we do not allow the plea of insanity, in any case, as a ground of acquittal, unless that insanity is of such a nature as to warrant the opinion that the individual did not intend to inflict the injury for which he is tried. And in case any degree of insanity appears to have actuated the individual, we inquire whether this disposition had ever been previously displayed; for in this case we hold the relatives or friends, or persons with whom he has lived, as accountable for not having given the magistrates due warning of his state of mind, so as that he should be put into confinement."

The travellers pressed in objection the various topics commonly urged respecting greater or lesser degrees of moral responsibility, capability of discerning good from evil, &c.; all which considerations the Southlanders, it appears, are accustomed to regard as entirely irrelevant. They maintain that criminal legislation has nothing whatsoever to do with moral retribution; the sole object of human laws being the prevention of crime, which can take place in all those cases, and in those only, where the intention of the agent (no matter how that intention originates) is directed towards the action to be prevented.

On the travellers expressing a strong desire to see their penitentiary, and examine its system of management; "We have many penitentiaries," said Sir Peter, "and in each of them the system adopted differs in some respects from that of others; for we hold it to be a subject of constant experiment to ascertain what mode of discipline may be the best fitted to secure the ultimate object at which we aim, which is, as I have just said, not the infliction of vengeance on the guilty, but the prevention of crime. I shall enable you, however, to judge of our system in this respect by taking you to visit our penitentiaries, according as you can command leisure.

"The systems pursued in some of our houses of correction," he added, "need, and, I trust, will receive alteration; but I hope you will not think me unduly partial in considering the very worst of our modes of secondary punishment far preferable to yours. Be assured we shall never undertake to found a new nation from the sweepings of our jails; receiving additional corruption—those of them who are capable of it—by unrestricted intercourse with each other during a four months' voyage, and their moral degradation completed by being reduced to a state of slavery; that is, by being consigned, as in your colony, to masters for whose benefit they are compelled to labour."

[The manuscript of the travellers did not contain very full information on the subject of penitentiaries, as there were many which they were still designing to visit. It would appear, however, that in some penitentiaries solitary confinement was the practice; in others, the culprits worked in companies; but, as in some of the American penitentiaries, total silence was enforced. Every man was made to work in a mask, in order that he should remain unknown to the rest, and thus escape the hardening effects which are the consequences of exposure of character.]

"There is one part of our system," said Sir Peter, "which I should mention to you, because it will serve to show you the diligence with which we apply ourselves to the continual improvement both of our civil and penal code. We hold it as a duty belonging to our judges and chief law officers, that they should discuss amongst themselves, from time to time, whatever alteration their experience in the administration of our laws may suggest to any of them as desirable. Whatever report is sent in by their united wisdom to parliament, is received with the utmost deference; and should any doubt remain as to the expediency of adopting their proposal, we invite some of the judges or law officers to assist us in our deliberations, by stating publicly the grounds of their recommendation. We allow them to debate freely, as if they were members of parliament; but of course we do not give them, as they are not members, any vote in the final decision. Indeed," he observed, "whenever we appoint (as we very constantly do) a commission empowered to collect information on any particular subject, and draw up a report recommending any new laws or practices, we allow the members of that commission to attend our parliamentary meetings and explain their own reasons. We conceive this can be best done by the same individuals whom we appoint to deliberate. We regard them as members of parliament in fact, *pro hac vice*, except that we do not give them a power of voting."

Newspapers, magazines, and other periodical publications are abundant and cheap in this country.

In the early part of the traveller's visit, Lieutenant R. Smith, having accidentally taken up a newspaper which lay on the table, was much interested in its perusal. The leading articles appeared to have been written with considerable discretion and good sense. He asked whether he might regard that paper as a fair specimen of the degree of talent which their newspapers generally presented.

The gentleman of the house replied that, in his estimation, that paper was rather the best of the day. Its conductor was a person of very high character and great attainments.

"You just saw him," he said, "riding by with our leading minister. We have several papers,—besides magazines and other periodicals,—conducted also with various degrees of talent, and of every shade and variety of political sentiment."

"In our country," said Lieutenant Smith, "conductors are not on such familiar terms with our statesmen; indeed they are seldom to be met in cultivated society. We think it the lowest department of literature. In fact, we scarcely deem the editor of a newspaper a literary man, or even a gentleman."

"I suppose then," said Mr. Bruce (their host), "that your papers are nothing more than a record of events and advertisements; and that they exercise no influence upon the general sentiments of the country."

"Quite the reverse," said the English travellers. "The newspapers produce a very decided influence; so much so that each party in the state takes care to hold some of them in pay, as advocates of the opinions which that party is anxious to maintain: and the editor of a paper not unfrequently prescribes the opinions or conduct which each party should adopt, many confining their reading almost exclusively to papers on their own side."

"This is very strange to us," said Mr. Sibthorpe, "and it appears perfectly inconsistent. Your refusal to associate with the conductors as gentlemen of reputation, must make them unworthy to be received into good society; most emphatically and particularly unworthy, not merely as unfitted for the company of gentry, but as undeserving of the respect of reputable people. Such, at least, seems to us to be the tendency of a ban of exclusion fixed on a class of persons such as these writers. A small shopkeeper indeed, or mechanic, though not admitted into the social circles of the higher classes,

for granted—as, till of late years, has been commonly done in Europe—that every one is qualified to teach anything he knows himself, that, from the highest to the lowest description of schoolmaster or tutor, every one is required to have gone through a regular course of training for that profession. Nor is the study of this art by any means confined to those who design professionally to engage in it; but some degree of it is considered as a part of a liberal education.

In some of the newly-settled, and, consequently, thinly-peopled districts, there are sometimes two (and, in some instances, even three) schoolhouses for one master or mistress. In such a case, the master attends at them by turns for half a week, or, if at a greater distance, a week. Sometimes the schools are kept up during the intervals by an assistant; sometimes even this is wanting; and the children remain at home half their time preparing lessons, in which they are examined when they return to school. It is held that one good master can do more service in two or three schools than two or three inferior ones. All parents and guardians are required to have the children under their care instructed. Any who may be too poor to afford the moderate cost of the humblest education are provided with it at the public charge; but it is very rare indeed that there is occasion for this, except in the case of the half-reclaimed aborigines.

The Southlanders were astonished to hear that, in what is called civilized Europe, a large proportion of the population should remain totally illiterate, "*like the savages*." When they were told that some persons in England dreaded the education of the labouring classes, as unfitting them for their station, and were disposed to apply the remark of Mandeville, that "if a horse knew as much as a man, I should be sorry to be his rider," they inquired how this was to be reconciled with the *political rights* which they were told were conceded to these very people; and how it could be safe to entrust *power* to those whom it was thought unsafe to instruct how to make a *rational use* of it.

"If," said they, "you are to keep men in slavery, like the domestic brutes, it may be the safest way to keep them in as brutish a condition of mind as you can; but brutes that are *not* enslaved are much more dangerous animals than rational beings. A horse is kept as a slave, and, however gently treated, is subjected to restraint, and compelled to labour for his *master's* service. It would be doubtless unsafe, and, what is more, *unjust*, to ride a horse if he *knew as much* as a man,—*i. e.* if he were a rational being, instead of a brute; but Dr. Mandeville ought to have remembered that, if a groom *knew no more* than a horse, he would be very unfit to be a *rider*."

They require, accordingly, that any parent who, from inconvenient distance of residence or any other cause, is unable or unwilling to send a child to school, shall provide for his instruction at home, and shall bring him to the periodical examinations of the school inspectors, who are appointed to visit the schools at stated times and examine the children. On being asked what would be done in the case of any parent's refusing instruction to his children, they said that no such case had occurred in their recollection; but that they conceived, if it should occur, it would be considered as a sufficient evidence of mental derangement. As for the *right* of a parent over his children, they utterly denied that his children *belong* to him in the same manner that dogs and cats and horses do, which he is at liberty to keep as mere pets and playthings, or as drudges, or to sell or drown if he finds himself overstocked. They hold that he has no more right to debar his children from instruction than to deny them proper food and clothing. To these last they have a fair claim—a claim enforced by law in all countries—as *animals*; to the other, as *rational* beings.

Female education also they attend to quite as much as Europeans, without confining it so much (among the upper classes) to mere showy accomplishments. Some of them laughed at our employment of the word "accomplishment," "which," said they, "signifies properly a *completion* of that which, by your account, is never *begun*." They cited a maxim which, they said, had been laid down by Aristotle,—that a people whose institutions pay no regard to women and children, are neglecting the *half* of the *present* generation, and the *whole* of the *next*. And they observed, that a child whose earliest years,—whose first impressions, and habits of thought and sentiments,—have been left to a mother who is wanting in cultivated understanding, and sound principles, and well-regulated feelings, will be very far from having a fair chance of turning out an estimable member of society.

On these subjects the travellers had much conversation with Sir Andrew Knox, who holds in the kingdom of Eutopia the office of inspector-general of education, nearly answering to that of minister of public instruction in some of the European states. In his observations on the conduct of the governments of Europe,—such as they had been three centuries back, and such as many of them appeared to him to continue in some measure still unchanged,—he remarked that nothing could be more completely the reverse of a wise and honest legislature than the attempt to make *belief* compulsory, and *knowledge not* compulsory.

"They enforced," said he, "the reception of 'true religion,'—that is, what the rulers regarded as such; and left it optional to learn, or to remain ignorant of, the difference between one religion and another. Even you, it seems, regard it as an intolerable encroachment on liberty to compel a person to learn his letters that he may be able to *read* the Bible; but you compel him to *believe* the Bible,—at least to profess his belief, or not openly to deny it. His *knowledge* of the book may be anything or nothing, just as he pleases; but he is required to acknowledge its divine authority and the correctness of your interpretation of it, or else you treat him as a helot or an alien, and exclude him from civil rights and power. He is not obliged to know whether Jerusalem is in the northern or southern hemisphere, or whether Mahomet lived before or after Christ; but he *is* obliged, under pain of punishments or civil disabilities, to think with you as to the Jewish, Christian, and Mahometan religions.

"Now this," he continued, "does seem to us most preposterous. I am not adverting now to its opposition to the principles of justice or of the Christian religion, but to common sense. An injunction which it is completely *in the power* of the subject to obey, and of the government to enforce, this governments do *not* issue; and one which the subject may be *unable* to obey, and which the government *cannot* fully enforce, *that* forms an essential part of their enactments; for to acquire a certain humble degree of *knowledge* (when government provides the means of instruction) is a command which the subject is clearly *able* to obey. He may, indeed, not think knowledge worth the trouble of study, and may be so brutish as to feel it a hardship not to be allowed to remain in stupid ignorance; but, unless he is a born idiot, he cannot say that it is *out of his power* to learn anything, or, again, that it is *against his conscience* to attempt it; nor, on the other hand, can he evade the requisition by *pretending* to have learnt what he has not, since his proficiency may be ascertained by examination. In the other case, *all* these circumstances are reversed. A man may be really *unable* to adopt the same view of religious truth as his rulers; he may feel it a *violence to his conscience* to profess their belief; and, lastly, he can always, if conscience does not stand in his way, make a false and hypocritical profession of a faith which he does not really hold.

"These governments, therefore, do *not* interfere where their interference would be, at least, both allowable and effectual—*we* think beneficial; and where their interference, as we think, is always noxious, but evidently may be both unjust and ineffectual, there they do interfere. Such a ruler, if he teaches his subjects hypocrisy, teaches them at least to be like himself; for his pretended zeal for God's honour and his people's welfare must be a mere specious cloak for his desire to uphold his own power in the most effectual and least troublesome way. As for true religion, if he had the least particle of it, or the least conception of its nature, he could not but know that it is a thing which cannot be enforced by law."

[Much more to the same purpose was urged by Sir Andrew Knox, who, like most of his countrymen, is tinged, as our readers will have perceived, with much of that peculiar habit of thought, derived from the founders of the colony, which many will probably be disposed to regard as eccentric enthusiasm and extravagance. The travellers laid before him, in reply, the arguments commonly employed in Europe (which need not be here repeated) for and against the existing principles of legislation, and the various modifications of these which have been introduced in the several European states.]

On something being said respecting the duty of a Christian ruler to maintain and enforce true religion, and respecting the conduct to be pursued by a Christian community, Sir Andrew observed that, in former times, there appeared to have prevailed among their European ancestors much confusion of thought on those subjects, which did not seem to be even now cleared up, but to be fostered by indistinctness of language.

"Ours," said he, "are 'Christian states,' in the sense that the *individual citizens* of them are Christians, but not in the sense of our *laws enforcing* the profession of Christianity, or of any particular religious persuasion. And although, in the sense first specified, our states might be called Christian, the phrase 'Christian community' conveys to *our* minds the idea, not of a state, but of a *church*; and to blend the two kinds of community into one, so as to give spiritual jurisdiction to the civil magistrate, to maintain religion by secular coercion, and to give those of a particular creed a monopoly of civil privileges and secular offices,—this we consider as changing Christianity into Judaism, and making Christ's kingdom one 'of this world,' which he expressly forbade."

"But is it not natural, Sir Andrew," said Mr. Sibthorpe, "that Christians, who have any real veneration for their religion, should wish to exclude from all share of political power in a Christian nation those who are not Christians, or who have depraved and corrupted the Christian faith?"

"Nothing could be more *natural*," replied he, "than that the Jewish people, when convinced, as the mass of them at one time were, of his divine mission, should wish to take Jesus and force Him to be their king, so that all who should have disowned his authority, or disobeyed his commands, would have incurred the penalties of treason. Nothing, I say, could be more natural than this; and thence it is that He was so earnest in renouncing all such pretensions, and prohibiting all such attempts: and experience shows how consonant to the character of the 'natural man' such a course of procedure has been ever since.

"But the question is not what is agreeable to human nature, but to the divine will. Our Master declared that his kingdom is not a temporal one; and we must not seek to do Him honour by running counter to his commands, so as to *make* it a kingdom of this world, and, as it were, 'take Him by force to make Him a king.' It cannot evince our veneration for Him to mix up religion with politics, when He and his Apostles neither did so nor permitted their followers to do so, though *they* possessed (what no human rulers can with truth pretend to) one ground of a claim to the right of enforcing true religion by civil penalties and disabilities, viz. the infallible knowledge of what *is* true religion.

"As for what you were saying of Christ's kingdom being indeed not of this world, but that, according to prophecy, the kingdoms of the earth are to become the kingdoms of the Lord, this we conceive must be understood of the *people themselves* becoming Christians; because we conceive that, if it were understood as authorising the state, as a civil community, to enforce and regulate Christianity by the secular sword, then Christ's kingdom *does* become a kingdom of this world. To set up a plea founded on a subtle verbal distinction where there is no real difference, reminds one (if I may be pardoned for using so homely an illustration) of the quibbling thief, who contended that he was unjustly charged with having carried off a horse; for that, in truth, it was the horse that had carried off him.

"The Jesuits of whom you have been telling me, according to the worst accounts given of their tricks and subterfuges, evasions and mental reservations, would be well deserving of their title,—they would be really and fitly 'companions of Jesus,'—if we could suppose Him and his Apostles to have secretly maintained a principle which goes to nullify practically (as soon as their followers should have gained sufficient strength) all their disavowals of political designs,—all their renunciation of temporal power as connected with their religion,—all desire to monopolize, as Christians, civil ascendency. They were accused of forbidding to give tribute to Cæsar,—of speaking against Cæsar, &c. Now, if you suppose that, when Jesus, in answer to such charges, said in a loud voice to the Roman governor, 'My kingdom is not of this world,' He had *whispered* to his disciples, 'This is only till you have gained sufficient numbers and strength; whenever and wherever you can become the predominant party, then draw the sword which I lately bid you sheathe, and enforce by civil penalties submission to my laws, and exclude by law from political privileges all who will not join your communion:'—if you suppose that while He publicly issued the injunction, 'Render to Cæsar the things that are Cæsar's,' He added as it were *aside*, to his companions, "Remember, however, that, as Cæsar is an idolater, you must hereafter make him embrace Christianity on pain of ceasing to be Cæsar; you must oblige him and all other governors and public officers, from the highest to the lowest, and all who would lay claim to any of the rights of citizens in any state where you can acquire political ascendency, to profess my religion; and *then* you must render to Cæsar the things that are Cæsar's; you must then 'render unto all their due,' after having first secured that none but those who agree with you in religion shall *have* politically, *any* due at all; you must 'submit yourselves to every ordinance of man,' after having first provided that every ordinance of man shall have submitted to you; you must consider 'the powers that be' as 'ordained of God,' after having monopolized them all for yourselves, carefully excluding unbelievers:—if, I say, you suppose this to have been the secret meaning and these the private instructions, of Jesus and his Apostles, while their openly avowed teaching was such as we find recorded, well surely may the most disingenuous of the *Jesuits* lay claim to their title."

"Can an unbeliever, then," said Mr. Sibthorpe,—"can even an atheist, in this country, rise to the highest offices?"

"I hope," said Sir Andrew, "such instances are rare; I know of none: but if you speak of the *possibility*, you should remember that in *every* country, even where the Inquisition exists, an atheist can, by disguising his real opinions, rise to any office, even that of Grand Inquisitor, or of Pope; which, indeed, you were lately telling me is suspected to be no such very rare occurrence."

"True," said Mr. Sibthorpe; "there is no law that can prevent hypocrisy, but what I meant is, an open and *avowed* infidel, or an advocate of extravagant corruptions of religion."

"If you mean to ask," said Sir Andrew, "whether *I would vote for* a man of that description, and whether a majority of electors would in any case be as likely to appoint him as one of opposite character, I answer at once in the negative; but if you are asking whether there is any *law to prohibit* my voting for such a man,—any *legal* incapacity on religious grounds,—we have no such law. As far as a man's religious opinions are concerned, his fitness or unfitness for any civil office is left to be decided by the judgment of the *electors*. Conviction of any *crime*, or ascertained deficiency in the requisite *knowledge*, alone disqualify a man by law for public offices.

"But it is important," added he, "to keep distinct two questions which, I observe, the modern Europeans, as well as our ancestors, have often confounded,—the question whether a person of such and such a description is or is not *fit*, or the most fit, to be appointed to such and such an office; and the question, whether the *electors* to that office shall be left to decide that point according to *their* judgment, instead of the legislators deciding it for them, and restricting their choice. How much shall be *left to the discretion* of the electors is one question; what is the wisest and *best use* they can make of their discretion is another, quite different, though often confounded with it.

"But, among us, it is in a *religious*, not a *civil* community—in a *church*, not in a *state*—that a man's religious qualifications or disqualifications are taken notice of in the laws of the community as determining whether he may or may not be one of its officers or one of its members. Our brethren in Europe, you seem to think, would, some of them, take for granted, from our acting on these principles, that we must be very indifferent about religion (though you, I rejoice to find, are ready to bear your testimony to the contrary); but they might as well conclude that we are indifferent about political affairs also, because we attend places of worship in which no political questions are discussed, and are members of Christian churches which do not intermeddle with politics. Indeed, I myself, as well as many others, am a member of an agricultural association also, in which neither political nor religious matters are introduced; and yet I hope many of us are good citizens, good Christians, and good farmers too.

"But since your people hold it to be allowable and right, and a duty, for a civil legislature in a Christian country to take cognizance of matters of religious faith, (which *we* think should be left between each man's conscience and the Deity,) you ought, methinks, to see nothing incongruous neither in a religious community taking cognizance of political matters also, and embodying in its creed and formularies decisions, not only of points of faith, but of points of politics. Thus you would have, not only Trinitarian or Arian churches, Calvinistic or Arminian, Episcopalian or Presbyterian churches, &c. but also, according to your phraseology, Tory churches and Whig churches, commercial-restriction churches and free-trade churches, &c. Parents, bringing their child to be baptized, would have to engage that he should be brought up in sound political as well as sound religious views; and to renounce in his name, not only sin, the world, and the devil, but also annual parliaments and vote by ballot, or some other political measure; and would have to be solemnly admonished, not only to bring him at a suitable age to be confirmed by the bishop, but also to have his vote duly registered. And a man would not be admissible at the eucharist unless he first declared his opinion, not only on the question of transubstantiation, but also on the mint regulations, paper currency, or any other such points on which the church or sect he belonged to should determine what was to be accounted orthodox. If you are struck, as you seem to be, with the incongruity and absurdity of such regulations and practices as these, you may form some conception how incongruous it appears in *our* eyes to mix up together *at all* the Christian religion and politics. In short," he added, in conclusion, "do but consider whether, among you, religion is considered as *a part of politics*, or *politics a part of religion*. If neither (which is what *we* hold), then your conduct is palpably inconsistent with your principles. If you hold religion to be a part of politics, what becomes of your *Christianity*? But if politics is held to be a part of religion, then such politico-religious creeds and formularies as I have just now been supposing, must be, not only reasonable, but even necessary."

"I admit," said Mr. Sibthorpe, "the absurdity of attempting by secular penalties to produce conviction of a religious doctrine, and the cruelty, as well as absurdity, of compelling outward profession of conviction. But how do you proceed in regard to the public *promulgators* of pernicious error? Is not a government bound to protect its subjects, not only from theft and violence, but also from having their minds, especially those of the young, the weak, and the ignorant, corrupted by every one who chooses to go about scattering moral and spiritual poison around him?"

"No one," answered Sir Andrew Knox, "would be allowed among us, under the plea of conscience, or any other, to incite men to a violation of the laws, to a breach of the peace, or to rebellion against government; else, indeed, men might be found preaching up theft and all sorts of crimes, like those Anabaptist sects that appeared before we left Europe, who inculcated community of goods and of wives, and I know not what abominations besides.

"But the practice, or the recommendation, of anything that is immoral, and so accounted by *all* good men of whatever religious persuasion, is clearly punishable by the civil magistrate. Nor can any plea of conscience be admitted as justifying abusive language against any class of religionists,—threats, violence, personal slander, or interruption of religious worship.

"But if any man peaceably sets forth his own views respecting religion, appealing to men's reason and conscience and the visible universe, or the Scriptures, we do not hold that the civil authorities are justified in going about to punish or silence him, or in excluding him from civil rights. Any *church*, indeed, to which he may have belonged will disown him as a member if he teach anything at variance with their fundamental religious principles; but this we do not regard as a *punishment* inflicted as for an offence, but rather as a *dissolution of partnership* between two parties who cannot agree as to the matter in which they were partners. He is excommunicated by his church only in the same manner as his church is excommunicated by him; but no *secular penalties* or privations are incurred by imputed religious error.

"For we consider that, in the first place, as the legislature is not infallible, there is no security that its enactments may not be on the wrong side; as there have been, indeed, both Trinitarian and Arian, Protestant and Popish laws and rulers: and, secondly, we consider that Christ and his Apostles, who did possess infallibility, deliberately chose to rest their cause on pure persuasion alone."

"But might it not be urged," said Mr. Sibthorpe, "that this would go to put an end to *all* legislation on all subjects, since no legislature can be infallible, even in political measures?"

"It is true," replied Sir Andrew, "that statesmen can lay no claim to infallible wisdom, even in their own department; and there is, accordingly, no country whose laws are, or *need be believed to be,* perfect.

"It is the duty of a good citizen to labour to bring about the improvement of any laws which he thinks inexpedient; but in the mean time (and *here* lies the important difference) he may, in almost all cases, obey the laws *with a safe conscience,* even such as he may not approve of; because they require only the *outward acts* of compliance, and not the inward assent and conviction of the mind. You had, for instance, formerly a law enjoining all men to put out their fires at the toll of the curfew-bell; it is now long since repealed. You had a law against selling game, which you have told us is abrogated. These laws may have been very inconvenient; but it could not be against a man's conscience to put out his fire or to abstain from buying and selling game, though it *would* have been to require him to declare his *belief* in the wisdom of those regulations.

"Hence it is that, imperfect as human legislation must be, laws, since they are essential to the existence of civil society, have the sanction of reason, and conscience, and Scripture in favour of submission to them, except in those cases where submission involves a violation of some prior duty; as if, suppose, we had a law enjoining us to hunt down the blacks, and kill them like wild beasts. But it is remarkable that almost all the cases where it does become a duty to resist the law, are those in which *religion* is concerned,—those, in short, in which the civil legislature has gone out of its own province; as when a man is required to profess or renounce, to preach or abstain from preaching, a certain religion; forbidden to instruct a slave in Christianity, (as, you say, was formerly the law at the Cape of Good Hope,) and other such injunctions.

"On these grounds," continued he, "we hold that all interference of the secular power to enforce the profession of 'true religion' and punish 'heretics,' or to give Christians, or any particular description of Christians, political ascendency on religious grounds, are adverse to the spirit and injurious to the cause of true religion, contrary to the commands of its Author, tending to impair the force of its proper evidence, and leading at once to oppression in one party, to hypocrisy in the other, and to unchristian rancour in both.

"These principles may be said, in some sort, to form a part of our national creed; for there is no one of our churches that does not maintain them, and inculcate the strictly voluntary character of true Christianity, and the spiritual, and not secular nature, of its Author's kingdom."

"But what would you do," said Mr. Sibthorpe, "if some church were to arise among you of opposite principles? Would you tolerate a sect whose religion forbade them to tolerate others?"

"That," said the other, "is certainly a shrewd question, and one which, I am happy to say, we can none of us answer from experience; as we have never had, and I hope never shall have, any such among us. I can, therefore, only speak from conjecture as to what conclusions we might come to in such a case. Probably, a good deal might depend on the *actual temper* of the persons who should hold in theory persecuting principles; for as men are too often worse than their principles, so, as you must be well aware, they are sometimes better; and if men of such principles were content to let their right and duty of persecution remain by some humane subterfuge in abeyance and dormant, we should probably let them alone. Much might also depend on their strength of numbers, on their power, as well as their disposition to do mischief. The cat appears to be much the same kind of animal as the lions and tigers we have read of; but, being too small to be formidable, is allowed to go loose about the house. I suppose it would be unsafe to extend the same *toleration* to a tiger.

"But on one point I think I can answer you, though still from conjecture, pretty confidently: if there *should* be any sect or class of men in one of our states whom we found it impossible to place, with due regard to our safety, on the footing of citizens, we should undoubtedly *part company*; we should banish them all, or we should imprison them all; nay, I think we should even put them all to death at once, were there no better alternative, rather than tolerate among us a race of helots or Gibeonites,—a degraded and disfranchised caste, especially one degraded on account of religious differences. *That* is contrary to all the principles, political and religious, which we have imbibed, as it were, with our very mothers' milk.

"There is, however, one point in which you were remarking, the other day, that our practice is more rigid than yours, and in which we might perhaps appear at the first glance to be, though in truth we are not, acting at variance with these principles. You were remarking that we are more prompt and daring than most Europeans in placing under restraint those who appear to be in a state of dangerous mental derangement. We hold it to be a benefit to the individual, as well as to the community, to confine and keep in order one who is palpably incapable of taking due care of himself; as, for instance, an habitual drunkard, who, though not otherwise mad, when sober cannot command himself so as to refrain from drinking, when liquor is within his reach, till he becomes no better than mad. Now, although no legal interference takes place to prevent a man from setting forth his own views of religion, or any other subject, and *appealing to the judgment* of his hearers, it is otherwise if he profess to have received a *divine revelation* and to be the bearer of an immediate message from the Deity. We do not pronounce such pretensions a *crime*; for the magistrate has no right to prejudge the question as to their *truth*, nor, for the same reason, are they considered as decisive evidence of insanity: but they do justify a certain degree of suspicion of it, and of such an insanity as may prove highly mischievous in various ways; and especially as being, above all other kinds of insanity, dreadfully infectious. Madmen of this particular class are, among persons of a nervous and excitable temperament, almost as dangerous as mad dogs.

"Now, any person professing, as the Apostles did, to have received an immediate divine commission to be special messengers of God, sent forth by his miraculous interposition with prophetic inspiration, must be either *a true apostle*, or an impious *impostor*, or else a man under *mental alienation*. That there can be but these three possible suppositions is evident; though it may not be evident, in any given case, *which* of the three is the true one. On the first supposition, the man is evidently entitled, *as soon as he shall have exhibited his credentials*, by displaying such miracles as are the 'signs of an apostle,' to high veneration, and diligent attention to what he is commissioned to declare. On the second supposition, he ought to be punished, on the same principle (only more severely) as pretended witches, conjurors, and other such cheats who practise on the credulity of the superstitious. On the third supposition, the man ought to be secluded and taken care of, and subjected to proper treatment for the cure of his disorder.

"In all cases, then, of professed inspiration and immediate divine commission, our laws enjoin solitary confinement, as perfectly suitable on any of the foregoing three suppositions. The person is subjected to no indignity or unnecessary pain; he is treated tenderly, and carefully provided for; but he is closely secluded from all but medical attendants and other official persons. We have a full trust that, if he be indeed a divine messenger, he will be miraculously liberated. We find in Scripture that this *was* done repeatedly; as in the case of the first imprisonment of the Apostles,—in that of Peter alone, afterwards,—and that of Paul and Silas. They were thus enabled both to execute their commission, and, by appeal to the miracle, to attest its truth. Nor do we consider that, as long as we abstain from all reproach or unnecessary violence, we should be doing any wrong even to real prophets, or presumptuously tempting the Deity; for it is contrary to all reason, and to all Scripture, to suppose that He ever did or can require implicit faith to be given to his ambassadors without furnishing them with testimonials; with credentials, to satisfy us that they really are sent by Him. To call upon a man pretending to inspiration to display a sensible miracle (as by a supernatural release from confinement) is no affront to God or man; it is only asking a professed ambassador for his credentials. But if, again, the man be either an impious impostor, or a lunatic, his confinement is, in the one case, a just, though very mild punishment, or, in the other, an act of kindness towards himself, as well as a removal of a nuisance to the public.

"Instances of the first class, I need hardly tell you, have not occurred; and there are not many of us, I believe, who expect that they ever will. But whatever may be thought of that last question, we all agree that it would imply want of faith, ignorance of Scripture, and folly, to doubt that God, if He did send us an inspired messenger, would fail to vindicate His own honour, and establish the prophet's mission, by miraculous proof; or to suspect that it could be displeasing to Him that we should insist on such proof, and refuse to incur the risk of *idolatry* in paying divine homage to a human device or delusion.

"In respect of the second class—impostors, our law has operated chiefly (as might have been expected) in the way of prevention. In a few instances, however, such men (having, for the most part, *secretly* circulated their pretensions among the credulous) have been induced, by the correction thus administered, to confess their fraud, and submit to the penalties of the laws enacted against common cheats.

"Of the third class—those under delusion, there have been a good many instances; and, in a large proportion of them, quiet seclusion and proper medical treatment have effected the restoration of reason: but some cases, as in all other kinds of derangement, prove incurable. There are also, by your account, in Europe also, such patients in almost every lunatic asylum,—imaginary apostles, prophets, and even deities. The only difference between us is, that *you* allow several of such patients to go at large and do mischief in the world, because *you* think it necessary to have fully *ascertained* that a man is deranged before you confine him; whereas we think it right to confine him at once, as soon as it is made evident that he is *either* deranged, or an impostor, or able (as a divine messenger, and therefore under a miraculous dispensation,) to obtain immediate release. In all these cases (and there can be no other supposition) we hold it manifestly allowable, and consequently right, to confine him."

It was in the course of this conversation, after the discussion of the foregoing and several kindred subjects, that one of the company made a remark respecting the views which had been presented to him of the history of Europe since their departure from it, as compared with its state at that time, and the general history of mankind.

"Our founders," he said, "appear to have had peculiar advantages, from which we have, I trust, derived some fruit, in the particular time and circumstances of their change of abode. They left Europe at the exciting period of the Reformation, which had shaken the hold that ancient opinions, habits, and institutions had long maintained over the human mind; when men's energies were roused, their imaginations kindled, and all their feelings highly stimulated.

"It is not to be wondered at, that, at such a period, many of the results should have followed which appear in Europe to have actually ensued. Some, we know, ran into the wildest extravagancies of innovation. Again, the fierce and obstinate opposition of others to every change—besides the malevolent passions thus called into play—appears to have driven many of the reformers to still greater excesses, or to have hardened them into greater pertinacity. And, moreover, many, frightened at the prospect of extravagant innovations, or weary of perpetual change, seem to have resolutely stopped short before they had fairly followed out their own just principles of a complete reformation; or even relapsed into the prejudices they had renounced, embraced anew the errors which had been exploded, and returned to the corrupt systems, which were standing, as it were, with their gates open to receive them.

"Our founders, on the other hand, after they had received the salutary stimulus, were removed out of the way of most of these evils by their retirement hither. Withdrawn from persecution and oppression, and furious controversy and religious wars, they were secured in a great measure from the fanaticism and the unchristian bitterness of spirit which these are so often found to generate. They were kept out of the way, again, of all temptation to return to the corrupt systems they had renounced, since no example of these remained among them; and were left calmly and peaceably to make trials of the application of their principles in practice, and to modify at leisure those principles according to the dictates of experience."

[Such is the substance of the conversation that passed on these subjects. The language is of course altered, in this and in the other conversations recorded, in order to render it more readily intelligible. It is, indeed, almost a *translation* that is given; not, indeed, from a foreign tongue, but from a peculiar dialect of English.

The greater part of what was said by the travellers, except what was necessary to make the answers intelligible, has been omitted, for the reasons already stated.]

# CHAPTER XIII

*Preachers.—Divine Service.—Divisions of the Bible.—Funeral Service.—Burial in Cities.—Absurd Interments.—Monuments.—Private Mausoleums.—Harmless Absurdities.—Church Endowments.—State of the Clergy.—Religious Communities.—Admission Fees to Institutions.—Ecclesiastical Societies.*

It happened in the earlier part of their visit, when the travellers were less familiar with the peculiarities of the Southland phraseology, that they were inquiring one day whether there was in the neighbourhood where they then were any *preacher* of more than ordinary celebrity, and were surprised at being answered that there were no preachers within two hundred miles. As they had, before this, attended public worship, they perceived at once that there must be some misapprehension. They found that "a preacher" denotes—according to its primitive sense—what *we* understand by a *missionary* among the heathen. "Expounding," "lecturing," "discoursing," are the terms used by them to denote what we call "preaching."

When the difficulty was surmounted which they felt at first in following what was said, from the novelty to them of the dialect, they were very well pleased with some discourses they heard, which appeared to them sensible, pious, and instructive; but they never heard any one who came up to the idea of what we call "a fine preacher," or "a very nice man," for the reason already mentioned in the notice of their parliamentary debates.

The strangers were at first puzzled by another peculiarity which they met with in their attendance on divine service. The minister referred, not to the chapter and verse of any book of Scripture, but to the page and line, or rather to what are *called* pages and lines; that is, certain equal divisions, which are indeed the actual pages and lines of their large editions of the Bible, but of course do not correspond with those of a different size. These artificial pages and lines, as they may be called, are marked by horizontal (P. 25,—) and vertical (L. 5. | ) lines, respectively. The origin of the custom, it seems, was, that their first edited translation having been *paged*, and subsequent editions being, for some time, fac-similes of it in point of size, the custom grew up,—indeed there is reason to think it was designedly encouraged,—of making the references to pages and lines; and these same arbitrary divisions were accordingly retained in subsequent editions. Generally, though not always, the chapters and verses are marked in the margin, for the convenience of scholars who may wish to consult some of the old editions of the Bible in the learned languages, or who may be reading, in old editions, some works of the earlier divines containing references to those divisions. For their own use, they consider their method as preferable to ours, inasmuch as their divisions are exactly *equal;* serve perfectly for the *use* intended,—that of facility of *reference;*—and carry on the face of them a plain indication that they are designed for no *other* use, and therefore cannot mislead the reader into the notion of their having a connexion with the sense, and being the work of the sacred writers, or designed by editors as a suitable distribution of the matter.

The funeral service varies in a slight degree in the rituals of the several churches; but in one point they all agree,—that in the prayers used, and in any discourse delivered on the occasion, no allusion is made to the particular individual deceased. The shortness and uncertainty of life generally,—a future state, and the requisite preparation for it,—with other such general topics, are the only ones allowed to be introduced. Any mention of, or allusion to a particular individual, in the way of panegyric or otherwise, on such an occasion, would be regarded as invidious and highly indecorous.

"When a man," they said, "has departed this life, to pronounce upon his condition in another world, or to pray that that condition may be altered, we regard as presumptuous, and especially unsuitable in a Christian congregation assembled for a religious purpose."

Their cemeteries are never contiguous to their places of ordinary religious worship, nor within any of their towns or villages; but at some little distance, and generally within, or adjoining, some park or other public pleasure-ground. They imagined it must be deleterious to the health of the Europeans to inhabit towns, the site of which consists in great measure of stratum upon stratum of decomposing animal matter, continually renewed and continually stirred up.

"We are well aware," they said, "what gave rise to the practice. It was the notion entertained by our ancestors (and, it should seem, by some of their European descendants) that demons are scared away by the sound of church-bells, by lustrations of holy-water, and the like; and that the departed, accordingly, derive from such things some kind of comfort and protection. We hold, however, (and we hoped our European brethren had long since come to the same conclusion,) that the only injuries of which a corpse is in any danger are from the plough or the spade, the carrion-crow, the swine, or the wolf;" (so they call the Dingo, the New Holland wild dog;)

"and that protection from these is to be found in stone walls, boards, and mounds of earth, not in any religious ceremonies.

"As for spiritual danger, we conceive that the body becomes exempt from everything of that kind, precisely at the moment life departs from it; and, accordingly, that religious appliances *then* employed resemble the practice of the savages, who clothe the dead body of a friend in the best skin robes they can procure, and bury it, surrounded with a store of food, and with all the implements of hunting and fishing. If these poor heathens were to go a step beyond this in absurdity,—if they were to refuse to supply a famished companion while living with needful food, clothing, and shelter, and then, as soon as he was dead, and no longer sensible of cold and hunger, were to *begin* to supply his dead body with provisions, which it could no longer use,—they would then be treating him, as some of our European forefathers treated themselves; who seldom or never, during their lives, frequented a house of worship to any profitable purpose, while they might have derived benefit from their attendance; but reflected with satisfaction on the idea that their dead bodies would be brought into the house of worship, and perhaps interred there, as soon as the time should have passed when their presence there would be of any avail.

"It is partly in order to guard against any relapse into such superstitions that we make it a rule never even to bring a dead body within the walls of a place of worship."

There are no monuments in their burial-grounds beyond plain slabs, containing the name of the person whose remains are interred, with the necessary dates, &c. But in other places they have monuments of the nature of cenotaphs, in memory of persons who have been in any manner so distinguished as to be allowed this posthumous honour, by the direction, or with the permission, of the civil authorities.

Statues are sometimes erected, in places of public resort, to men of high eminence: but usually the memorial consists in an inscription (sometimes accompanied with decorative sculpture) placed on the *house* in which the person in question was born, or lived, or died; or on any public building, such as a college, or library, or the like, which was in any way connected with his useful labours. In all cases, any monument so placed as to meet the public eye, cannot be erected without the permission of the proper authorities; whose approval of the inscription, decorations, and all the particulars, is essentially requisite.

"If a man chooses," said they, "to erect within his own private house or garden the most extravagant mausoleum in honour of some ancestor, and to cover it with inscriptions of the most fulsome and groundless panegyric, he is quite at liberty to do so. We do not profess to make laws to prevent a man from playing the fool in private; but whatever is obtruded on the *public* eye is fairly placed under public control. And monuments," they added, "when thus duly regulated, constitute a useful kind of record of departed worth, and of the several degrees and kinds of it; the utility of which record would be greatly impaired if mixed up and interlined, as it were, with the aberrations of the private partiality, or ostentation, or absurdity of individuals.

"It is the same," they said, "with titles of honour, and decorations of office borne by the living. If a man has a fancy to wear in private a dressing-gown decorated like a robe of state,—to have his easy-chair in his study made after the fashion of a regal throne,—to make his own family in private call him your lordship or your majesty, or to amuse himself at his own home with any such folly, the laws would not take cognizance of his harmless absurdities; but if he were to do all this in public, he would not be allowed thus to go about to break down all distinctions of rank, dignity, and office, by assuming what did not belong to him. Now, we consider that monumental honours, when displayed before the public, are a kind of public posthumous dignities; over which, accordingly, the Public has a just right of control."

All the churches are possessed of endowments (greater or less); generally, though not exclusively, land, which are held by bodies of trustees (variously constituted), recognised as corporations; these receive and distribute the revenues, and, in some churches, have the nomination to benefices; in others, this is placed in their hands conjointly with the overseer (somewhat answering to bishop), or council of overseers, of the church.

What is called among us the 'voluntary system,'—the maintenance of the minister by the voluntary contributions of his congregation,—is not only unknown, but distinctly prohibited, in all the churches, by a regulation which forbids the minister even to accept any kind of gratuity from his flock, or to derive any profit from the letting of seats, or any other such source.

Dr. Campbell, a clergyman and theological professor at one of their seminaries, from whom among others their information on these subjects was derived, observed, that he was not sure (as the experiment never had been—and he hoped never would be—tried among them) whether any of their States would even tolerate a religion whose ministers were to be maintained by the congregations as hired servants.

"A pastor," said he, "appointed by the people,—which is bad enough,—or removable by the people,—which is still much worse,—or supported by the gifts of the people,—which is far worst of all,—has everything to encounter that can tend to make him what he should not be; and that can expose him to suspicion of this, even if undeserved; and that can lower his character, and lessen his deserved influence, if he is such as he ought to be. No plan," he added, "could possibly be devised more calculated for debasing and corrupting both the clergy and people, and for perverting religion, and turning it into a source of evil, instead of good, to both. The people would be taught to seek for, and their pastor (I should rather say, their *servant*) tempted to supply,—instead of honest and profitable instruction and seasonable admonitions,—flattery to their prejudices,—indulgence to their vices,—encouragement to their superstitions,—assistance and counsel in political schemes and party machinations,—amusing theatrical excitement to itching ears,—and flattering delusions, as opiates to the soul, instead of wholesome truth."

On its being remarked, in reply, that many persons in England contend for the benefit of making a minister's income depend, in some degree at least, on his own exertions, and are accustomed to adduce instances of the inefficiency of some whose revenues are secure and independent, Dr. Campbell replied that it is true such instances do occasionally occur, and are much to be deplored.

"But, after all," added he, "we ought to remember that, bad as it is for a minister to be useless, *useless* is the *best* thing *such* a minister *can* be. A clergyman who is capable of being stimulated to exertion *only* by motives of interest, and is careless and apathetic when *that* is wanting, had much better be *left* careless. When gain does rouse such a man to exertion, he will most likely exert himself as a demagogue or a mountebank. A man whom neither conscientious motives, nor desire for the respect and esteem of good men, can rouse to efficiency in doing good, is very likely to become an active doer of evil, if he have any dormant energies and talents that can be roused at all."

On inquiring whether the governments, accordingly, insist on paying all ministers of religion who are not otherwise provided for, the travellers were informed that Government never pays any. Occasionally, indeed, grants of state-lands are made to various public institutions, and to religious ones among the rest; but this is always by a distinct act of each legislature in reference to the circumstances of each case that is brought before them. But any persons who can raise among themselves, and from their well-wishers, funds towards building and endowing chapels, &c. and who prefer forming themselves into a distinct religious community, never find any considerable difficulty in obtaining a charter of incorporation for such trustees as they appoint. And it has often happened that, by accessions of donations or bequests from time to time, and also of members, some, both ecclesiastical and also academical corporations, have, from small beginnings, grown into considerable importance.

"The voluntary system," said Dr. Campbell, "which we condemn, is not voluntary gifts towards a common fund for an endowment *in perpetuity*, but voluntary payments from time to time to a particular minister for his yearly or weekly maintenance by his people,—by those, I was going to say, who are placed under him; but, it should rather be, *under whom he is placed*."

It is a custom, it seems, for those admitted on any academical or ecclesiastical foundation as partakers of the endowment, to contribute themselves towards the fund, by paying a certain admission-fee, as it may be called, on entrance. In the greater part of the institutions whose endowments are sufficient for their objects this is little more than a nominal payment, a sort of ceremonial acknowledgment, trifling in amount: but in less amply endowed societies it is something considerable; in those whose common funds are still smaller, it is more; and in some,—chiefly such as are in their infancy,—a man has to pay, on being admitted a fellow, an associate, a pastor, or whatever it may be, of one of these colleges, or churches, &c. a sum equal to, or even exceeding, what his maintenance derived from the society will probably cost, according to the principles of annuity-office calculations. In such a case, the advantages sought by the man or woman who is a candidate for admission (for there are several female institutions of this kind) are the pleasure and honour of being admitted into a society, perhaps in high repute for the intelligence, worth, knowledge, and agreeableness of its members,—(the same objects that make it in England often a matter of earnest competition to be elected into a particular club,)—the conveniences, sometimes, of a common library, museum, table, &c.; so that a person who may have paid more than he or she will actually cost the society, may yet have made a very good bargain in the purchase of a comfortable and respectable maintenance; and, lastly, the advantage of the purchase of a kind of *annuity*; paying down a certain sum, and being secured, as far as a decent subsistence, against all chances, by insuring a maintenance during life, or during single-life, according to the regulations of each society.

The fellowships, &c. of *colleges* are, for the most part, held during celibacy only; and some of them make little or no provision for any but those actually resident. Persons admitted on the foundation of *ecclesiastical* societies, as ministers or other officers, receive a stipend for life, unless regularly expelled for misconduct.

There are several further particulars relating to these matters, on which, as has been already mentioned, Mr. Sibthorpe hoped to obtain fuller information.

# CHAPTER XIV

### Letter of Paul Wilkins.

We shall close these extracts with a letter, which we have had permission to publish, from one of the exploring party, Paul Wilkins, the sailor formerly mentioned, written after his return to Sidney to his parents in England. Our reader will perceive from this letter that a part only of the travellers had returned; two of them having determined to prolong their stay in the newly-discovered colony, in order to gain a fuller acquaintance with its singular customs and institutions.

The letter is printed exactly from the manuscript, because, if any alterations had been made,—even though extending only to the style and orthography,—or any omissions even of the most trivial matters, the reader might have been left in doubt what degree of liberty might have been taken with the original. And errors in language or in spelling, such as may be expected in the composition of a person of ordinary education in humble life, can excite no disgust or contempt; and must disarm criticism, when occurring in a familiar letter designed for the perusal of his own domestic circle, by one who never thought of aspiring to come before the public as an author. Taking into account the station and circumstances of the writer, there is nothing, we conceive, that will be thought to do discredit to his head or heart.

*"Sydney, Novr. 23rd, 1835.*

"Dear Father & Mother

"This comes with my Love, hoping to find you a live & all well, as it leaves me thank God, which I never expected sometimes to come Back a live from a long and peralous Expidition into the Interier. But am happy to say we suckseded & have been to the most Wonderfull country I ever see in all my Voyages. I sho'd never have done if I was to go to tell you every thing, but as their is a Vessel just going to Sail, and I can send this by a safe Hand I take up my pen to give you some a count of it.

"I hardly know how to be gin my Head is so full of all the queer things I see. The two Lieut. Smiths who you remember my shewing you one of them last time I was at Home, fine dashing felowes they are as ever trod a plank, they and Mr. Sibthorp of the Colony and Mr. Jones, they ingag'd me as a tendant to exploar in the Interier on a new plan of their own. They said as no great Navigable rivers has been found by coasting Expiditions, the only chance was to try in land, and if they met with any considarable Stream to follow it till it come either to the Sea or a great Lake which some thought there is a great in land Sea in the Interier. So says they cout kick out they wou'd find wether their is one or no. So off we sat & took with us the frame work of a Canoe flat bottomed by reason of the Shallows were we was to Embark. And when we come to the Lake which it is a kind of swamp like, more weeds than Water, we put our canoe to gether & coverd it with Bark of Trees & got in our Stores. Their was no room for much Provisions but we trusted to our Guns & Fishing tackle, all the Party are pretty good shots, & your Humble Servant no bad Hand tho' I say it at striking Fish or Hook & Line.

"It was hard work for some days, we were like a dab chick scufling & flutering along among the Flags & Mud, & then we got into clearer water & made Sail at a good rate, & then into a River which we thought this will bring us to the sea, But no we got into more Lakes & swamps, and then river a gain & so on, & then we had to get out and track the Canoe with Ropes to steddy its coarse along the rapids, & once we was forced to carry it overland to a void the Falls. And some times we never thought but what we sho'd be lost an starved in the Wilds, all the country round nothing but Rocks & Sands. But we all kep up a good Heart, no want of Pluck among the Gent men, and I can't say we wanted for Vittles only going without Bread mostly thanks to the Fish & Wildfowl.

"I sho'd never have done if I was to tell you All. Well after better than a Month were do you think we come to at last, why to a Colony of White men, that had been hid like in the Wilds best part of three Hundred years & never seen no Christian peple all that time only them selves. Its true I a sure you, & its compewted theirs nearer 4 milian than three totell number of Soles in the Country. How serprised we was to see em & hear em hail us in English, for their of English Dissent mostly only some mixture of Duch & German & Swiss. Its an odd sort of English too they speak, but we got usd to it in a little wile, their lingo isnt worse than broaed Scoch or Yorkshire.

"Well you may be sure if they wonderd to see us we was wondring how they come their. And it seems they came out in former times when their was great trubles in Europe to make a settlement and live in Piece & Quiet,

And their Vessels was driven on the coast, & they got a shore & landed all their stores safe, & then went up & setled in the Interier, being they found the coast unhealthy. Its a fine Country they have got to now, as big I am thinking as Great Briton & Ireland put to gether, for they arnt no ways prest for room, but make a new Setlement were they likes. They treated us very kindly in deed & seamed glad to see us as if we had been brethren like, as they say'd. And very good Towns & good Living their is among them, tho' they arnt quite so high civilised as English Peple, as stands to Reason being they have livd so long out of the World like.

"And some queer ways they have among them to be sure, quite different from ours. Theirs not a bit of Bacca to be had for love nor money, nor Grog neither, as for Rum or Whisky or the like they dont know what it means. I usd to tell em how theyd stare if they was to come among us & see writen up every were Dealer in Tea Coffee To Bacco & Snuff, & Dealer in Spirtuos Liquors, for they havent nothing of the kind. But how ever they have good ale that I must say & Wine & Cyder to plenty, & very hospy table peple, but no way given to liquor, I never see a drunken Man all the time, & they say its like the Savages to get drunk. And theirs truth in that I can testyfy, for those Black felows will drink as long as they can stand in the Colony and longer two if they can come at liquor. They say wo'dnt you reckon it a Great Miss fortune if you was to go out of your Mind & have to be put in a mad House, and if a Man gets drunk he goes out of his mind, & ought to be shut up in confinement, & they say if a Man was a reglar drunkard they wou'd shut him up two.

"They are good farmers I must say & good breeders too. you tell Mr. Evans, & my respects to him hope he is well & all his family, I haven't for got all the farming I learnt under him tho' I was but a lad, I wish he cou'd see the fine cows like the Holderness in the low grounds, and a breed like the alderney on the Mountaneous parts, & sheep to both long & short wool, such fleeces as I think he never see. But as for Mutton I can't speak, for only think they never heard tell of Mutton, for theyd think it a most as big a sin to kill a Sheep or a Bulock & eat it as we shou'd to kill a Christian & eat his flesh like the Cannibles does. Theirs a queer peple for you. But they goes out hunting the Wild Cattle and wild Hog, theyve plenty of them, & they dont object by no means to a bit of wild pork or beef.

"A nother fancy of theirs is they never will have Joints of meat servd up nor any thing done hole, not a pig or a foul or a fish if its ever so small, but all done in chops or Hash or the like of that. And they said we must be like the savages to feed on hole carcasses & Limbs of Annimals, as Egles & Woolves does. They calls a Dingo a woolf, thats the Newholland wild dog.

"We went out with them several times, Hunting & shooting. They have guns only not so good as ours, but they shoot with Bows & Arows be sides, & wonderful good shots some of em is. Sometimes when we went out we had only to look on at them shooting, because they woudnt have no firing for fear of scaring away the game. But sometimes we had a grand Battoo & then all had guns & our Gentmen shot as well as the best of them. Mr. Jones made a present of his double baril Gun to one Gentman of the Country & mightyly pleased he was, for their workmen arnt up to a double Baril. And I shewd them a thing or too about the build & rigging of their fishing-boats that they wasnt up to. And very great full & handsome they was I must say, for they gave me as much in their money & other things as comes to better than 50£ besides several curosities as a sort of Keep sake like, I got new rigged from top to toe all in cloaths of their fashion hat & all & a comical hat you'd think if you was to see it.

"Mr. Jones he said at first all the peple looked like musheroms they have hats as big as a small table, but that is to keep off the sun which it is very glearing in new Holland.

"Then it was so strange to hear all about Kings & Sennates & Parliments & Piers & Lord mayers, just like being in a new World like. The thing is they have eleven states something like the States of America, only some is kingdoms & some is republicks & what not. I harly knew weather I was a sleep or a wake, it seam'd a kind of dream like.

"Then I went several times to parties of pleasure something in the Nature of our Wakes they calls them Rebels & I a tended my Masters to wait upon them at some of the Rebels of the Gentry, and high & low their was plenty of mirth at all. But the first time I went with the Gentmen I thought their was to be a Ball or the like of that just as the gentlefolks have in England, & sure anuff their was Gentmen & Lords & Lady's a playing at Bowls or something like, & some shooting at a target, & some at other games in the nature of tenis & trap-ball, all as fond of the sport as boys & girls, &

they all grown up Gent folks & no mistake. And the best of it is they thinks dansing is only fit for children & Savages. It's as true as I am sitting hear.

"Its a fine country as I told you for pastur & corn & for gardens & orcheards to, & we see a good shew for fruit, only they havent got all the fruits as are in our colonies, being I suppose they wasnt known in former Times. And they are great Hands at Iragation as its calld thats leting the Water over the Land same as our Water Meadows, They'll dam up a stream were it comes down from the high Ground, & So let it off by Canalls, & smaller Canalls out of those & so on, & then lower down there will be a nother dam, & so the River keeps wasting a way as it goes on, & some never gets to the Sea a tall. And its my belief they are one cause why no body has found any large river falling into the sea, for they say themselves, some that was in former times good sizd Rivers flowing to'rds the coast are now next to nothing. There is a great many Lakes tho' & a sight of fine Fish in them, its wonderful to see how some of them will shoot fish in the shalows with Bow an arow. I never see the like, but for striking them with a spear I was up to that as well as them, & hook & line two.

"And they always serves up fish for second coarse, when theirs any meat for dinner or foul as their generly is, fresh or salt, pork beaf ducks & Geese plenty, then up comes fish after meat, & soupe last of all, & only think chese the first thing of all to begin dinner. They say its a wonder how any Body can degest chese after a Meal, & to be sure there is a saying that chese dejest all things but it self. But its all contrary to our ways as many things is hear, perhaps youll think it stands to reason were the north wind is hot & the south cold & Chrismas come in summer & the shortest day falls in June, tho' the folks dont walk with their heads down & heals up in the air neither as the old nurses used to tell us.

"Well I cant tell you all nor half, but I must tell you of one great curosity we all went to see, near the town of Bath called Mount perril, its a good high mountain & they say was in times past a Burning mountain, & there is great caverns in the side, & out of some of them their ishues a noxuous vaper like what Ive heard talk of in coal pits wich they calls it chokdamp. We went a long with the worshipfull Christopher Adamson one of the Sennaters as they call im of the state of Bath, & stood a top of a cliff over one they calld the Gobbling cave, & let down in an iron Great a litle heap of dry chips & brush wood all a light & blazing, & wen it got into the caves mouth out it went as black as night jest as if you'd sousd it into the Sea, only there was no Hiss, and they said if any body was to go close to the mouth at some times hed drop down sufficated by the vaper. And in times past they said it was a fassion for Gentmen & Ladies two, if they had a Quarril to challenge one a nother to go their, by way of fighting a Dual, they calld it an Or Dual & they behovd to go to gather past the Gobbling cave & take their chance wich of 'em sho'd be Sufficated, & some times both. I said I thou't it better than that or pistols either, to go and box it out fairly & then shake hands, & be freinds, tho' to be sure that wouldnt do for the Ladys. But however theres no Or Duals now no kind of Duals at all their now a days. Their all to gather a very peicable well behaved set of peple as ever I see, And their a well looking peple to, tho' some of them has a lick of the Tar brush as they say in the West Indies that is a mixture of Black blood in them, but they ar'nt no ways asham'd of it, for they say their not savages at any rate, & all men are children of Adam.

"Well I must conclude tho' I havnt tolld you half what I see, So Mr. Sibthorpe he was for staying a bit longer if he could but let all our freinds know we were safe, for they wo'd be sure to give us up for lost. So it was setteld for Mr. Sibthorpe to stay & Lieut Robt Smith, to stay behind & the rest of us to return, and a long with us young Squire Adamson a son of the old sennator. And there was several more talkd of coming to visit Sidney & paraps England to, along with Mr. Sibthorpe. Well it was about six weeks in all we'd been thear, geting toards the latter part of Octr wen we set off to return and the peple had sent a party on befour, with two Canoes & provisions to wait for us some way on, & we went over land on horse back by a short cut that the Hunters knew of. And that saved us a good bit. And when we imbarked we knew the rout & saved a deal of time that we had lost in coming. But then again we was forced to land in some places were the water was to shalow, or dried up since we was thear be fore. And some hard work we had to get a long over the rocks & weeds. So after great fatigue it was passed the middle of Novr before we ariv'd, which we did all well thank God, & glad our friends was to see us, for they given us up for Lost.

"And so now as their's a Vessel to Sail Day after To-morrow Morning I send this in haste hoping it will find you well & my Love to sister Jenkyns and her Husband hope is doing well & the boys who I supose they are grown out of my knowlege, And love to sister Nancy hope she's a good girl & must be a help to you as you get old. So no more at present from your dutifull

"Son dear Father & Mother

"Paul Wilkins.

"P. S. I send Nancy a work bag I brought with me, made & embroided by a southland woman, she'd never gess what its made of, for its the poutch under a Pellicans Throat, what he keeps fish in. I send you also some peaces of their Money what they Give me, it is nothing very perticuler curious only for the shape, wich all they have is the Same that is not Round peaces like ourn is but Oval, wich they say it is not liabel to role away and be Lost if you drop a Peace, & so I think it is Better."